12-87

To Chuck —

Thanks for the umbrella;
I needed it last year —

A smile to you —

Yours

THE COMPLETE BOOK OF
COCKPITS
BY DON DWIGGINS

No. 2332
$39.95

THE COMPLETE BOOK OF
COCKPITS
BY DON DWIGGINS

TAB BOOKS Inc.
BLUE RIDGE SUMMIT, PA. 17214

Modern Aviation Series Editor: Joe Christy

Aviation Editor: Steven H. Mesner

FIRST EDITION

FIRST PRINTING

Library of Congress Cataloging in Publication Data

Dwiggins, Don.
   The complete book of cockpits.

   Includes index.
   1. Airplanes—Cockpits. 2. Aeronautical instruments.   I. Title.
TL681.C6D87   629.135   81-18378
ISBN 0-8306-2332-9   AACR2

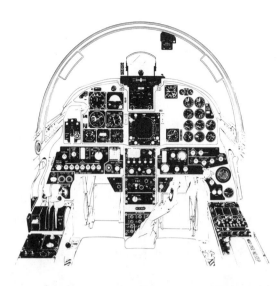

Contents

Motorglider–Rutan VariViggen; VariEze; Long-EZ; RAF-40 Defiant–Spencer Amphibian Air Cars–Stits Flut-R-Bug–Steen Skybolt–Stolp Acroduster Too SA750; SA-500 Starlet–Turner T-40B–Teenie Two-Thorp T-18 Tiger–Van's RV-3–Volmer VJ-22 Sportsman–Wh-1 Wendt Traveler–Wittman W-8 Tailwind–Woody's Pusher–Zenith CH-200

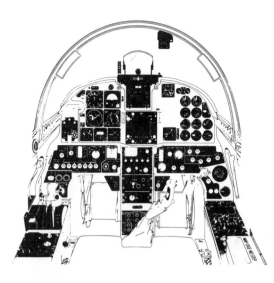

Introduction

Perhaps the title of this book is a misnomer—a *really* complete book of cockpits would be so voluminous as to make it not only dull reading but also highly repetitive. There are pilots who will tell you that "You've seen one cockpit, you've seen 'em all!" *Not true.* While basic types of aircraft do have many similarities in cockpit design, there are subtle differences that spell individuality. Government agencies have tried to enforce certain standardization of cockpit design and instrument panel layouts in the interest of safety, and this is good.

Modern technology, however, is highly influenced by human tastes and trends, as well as by sales gimmicks that are offered to appeal to the customer who wants an aircraft that suits his or her personal fancy and by the kind of flying expected to be followed. Pilot comfort and efficiency are foremost design criteria, along with safety. If you plan to fly high, far, and fast, you may well want to have your cockpit pressurized, or at least have supplemental oxygen available to keep you fresh and alert. If you're just a weekend pleasure pilot, you will not require sophisticated navigation and communication gear such as RNAV or multichannel NAV/COMMs. A magnetic compass, road map, and simple two-way radio equipment may suffice.

Military pilots require far more sophistication, of course, designed for their particular missions such as strategic bombing, escort fighter missions, interception, reconnaissance . . . you name it! I won't go into the military side of the story too deeply here, for you are more likely a homebuilder interested in designing and building your own aircraft or a general aviation pilot interested in familiarizing yourself with the various cockpit layouts available so that you can make the transition from the trainer in which you learned to fly to a different type aircraft. A certain number of military cockpits will be shown, and it is hoped that these will be of interest and use to model builders.

Essentially, aircraft instruments are extensions of a pilot's senses, refinements of his vision and other sensory perceptions that supply the information he needs to feel at home in the sky at all times. The following chapters look back to the beginnings of human flight and trace the development of cockpits to today's sophisticated "offices" where one or more airmen spend their hours.

Acknowledgments

Without the assistance and cooperation of many individuals, firms, and organizations, it would have been impossible to compile the material for *The Complete Book of Cockpits*. Special thanks go to the U.S. Air Force, Navy, and Marine Corps; contractors for military, air carrier, and general aviation aircraft; and avionics manufacturers whose products appear herein. Among them are:

Steve Caine, Frank Pedroja, and Bill Robinson, *Beech Aircraft*

Dick Tipton, *Bell Helicopter Textron*

Robin K. Beggs and Thomas R. Cole, *Boeing Company*

Madelyn Bush, *Boeing Vertol*

Loretta Kelly, *Cessna Aircraft*

Dan Synovec, *Douglas Aircraft*

Roy Wendell, *Fairchild Republic*

Jim Greenwood and John Meyer, *Gates Learjet*

Z. Joe Thornton, *General Dynamics*

Kris Lane, Lois Lovisolo, and "Schoney" Schonenberg, *Grumman Aerospace Corporation*

Hal Klopper, *Hughes Helicopters*

Robert Ferguson and Floyd Nelson, Jr., *Lockheed Corporation*

Harry S. Gann and Doree Martin, *McDonnell Douglas*

Lisa Vacquez and Terry White, *National Aeronautics and Space Administration*

Dorothy Cochrane and Robert Mikesh, *National Air and Space Museum*

Joseph Ponte, Jr., *Piper Aircraft*

J. David Hughes and A.J. Marcus, Jr., *Rockwell International*

Lt. Col. Eric Solander, *U.S. Air Force Office of Public Affairs, Magazine and Book Division*

Tommy L. Wilson, *Vought Corporation*

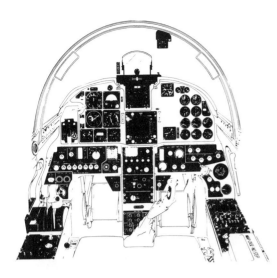

Chapter 1
String on a Wing

On Friday the Thirteenth of February, 1981, Civil Aeronautics Board crash investigators combed through the wreckage of a 12-place, four-engined Lockheed Jetstar that had plunged to earth on a heavily-wooded peninsula jutting into Rye Lake near Westchester County Airport, 15 miles north of New York City. What they were trying to determine was why the pilot, attempting an instrument landing in rain and fog that had cut visibility to less than a mile, had strayed from the glide path, sheared off huge treetops, crashed, and burst into flames.

The accident took eight lives—pilot, copilot, and six executives of Texasgulf, Incorporated—at a spot two miles short of the runway, a site eerily known as Dark Hollow. The victims included Texasgulf's Board Chairman Charles F. Fogarty, age 59, chief executive officer of the worldwide oil and mining concern, and other high executives of the business.

The Jetstar was equipped with the latest avionics equipment for bad-weather flying and was in contact with the airport's control tower as it approached the 6500-foot main runway. The jet was highly visible on the tower's radar screens as it groped its way through swirling mists, following the electronic glide path, when suddenly, with no warning, it vanished from the radar screen.

CAB investigators determined that both pilots—J. Morgan Gregory, age 63, the captain, and his copilot, Shanley Sorenson, age 42—were veteran airmen, highly proficient in IFR (Instrument Flight Rules) flying. They were well aware that the crash of a corporate jet was a rarity and account for less than 10 percent of all aviation accidents. Scheduled airlines have a far lower accident rate, while personal aircraft account for close to 90 percent of all accidents.

In a study by the National Transportation Safety Board (NTSB) of accidents categorized by pilot certificate, by far the greatest number involved private pilots operating fixed-wing aircraft in daylight hours. In 1979 alone, a total of 4238 general aviation accidents occurred, of which 658 involved a total of 1311 fatalities.

Pilot Error

In an NTSB report on aircraft accidents for the year 1976, pilot error emerged as the most common cause of accidents that resulted in fatalities, and a look at the five most frequent causes included (1) failure to obtain/maintain flying speed, (2) spatial disorientation, (3) continued VFR flight into adverse weather conditions, (4) failure to see and avoid other aircraft, and (5) failure to see and avoid objects or obstructions.

So what does this tell us?

First, it's the old argument of whether guns kill people or people kill people: airplanes and powerplants on occasion do get the blame for a fatal accident (as when a crankshaft breaks and the engine shakes loose), but by and large it is the *pilot* who gets into trouble. All accidents, both fatal and non-fatal, form another category of this NTSB study, which reveals that the prime cause of aircraft accidents is *"inadequate preflight preparation and/or planning"* followed by guess what?—*"mismanagement of fuel."*

Whether a pilot forgets to switch over from an empty gas tank, forgets to allow for strong headwinds, or makes some other mistake that leads to disaster, the trouble usually originates in the cockpit. For example, most light twins are unable to maintain altitude flying at gross weight when one engine fails. As a Federal Aviation Administration Safety Specialist once told me: "When one engine quits, the other engine takes you directly to the site of death and destruction."

Many, if not all, accidents blamed on pilot error *could have been avoided* had the pilot kept a careful check of instruments, switches, and gauges placed in the cockpit for his protection—oftentimes an admittedly confusing array of information inputs that requires a systematic approach to their utilization.

Cockpit Checklist

The most effective way of looking over the scores of such instruments and other items is by using the common *cockpit checklist*, an enumeration of the most vital things to take care of during preflight, inflight, or postflight periods. Mnemonic code words in the form of acronyms or other easily remembered arrangements may be used to assist the pilot in completing his cockpit check efficiently. One is GUMP (*Gas, Undercarriage, Mixture, Pitch*); another is simply TMPFF (*Trim, Mixture, Pitch, Fuel, Flaps*).

But this is not enough. Handy, yes, but not all-inclusive; hence, regular, periodic cockpit checks are used to insure that the aircraft will keep functioning while the pilot attends to other chores, such as navigation and communications. Later chapters look at some of the more sophisticated cockpit aids, such as fuel-flow meters, autopilots, and RNAV (area navigation) installations.

For now, let's look back across the years to a time when aircraft were flimsy affairs of bamboo and piano wire, covered with linen and powered with dubious powerplants.

In a sense flying was far simpler then, if not exactly safer. The modern airman must be highly trained to utilize all the cockpit aids available to him, properly, and NTSB accident investigators often can only guess why a pilot, such as the officer in command of the Lockheed Jetstar, let his aircraft stray from the straight and narrow. One might guess that a sudden downdraft forced the aircraft below its glidepath into the wooded hillside, but a guess is not enough. Did he misread the glideslope indicator? Did a fuel tank become exhausted at a critical moment?

The First Aircraft Instrument

Such complexities did not exist when aviation was young. Let's look back to September 17, 1911, when a handsome, cigar-chewing, 6-foot-4 pilot named Calbraith Perry Rodgers took off from Sheepshead Bay in Brooklyn, New York, in a Wright biplane. On November 5, 49 days later, he landed the crate in Pasadena and was the first man ever to cross the United States by air.

Rogers' sole flight instrument was simply a piece of string tied to a wing strut. By glancing at the way it fluttered back in the slipstream, he could tell fairly well whether his aircraft was slipping or skidding sideways or pitching up or down more than necessary.

The piece of string helped Rogers keep his ship flying in the proper *attitude* (one of the secrets of modern-day instrument flying, incidentally), but he carried no radio to follow a navigation beam as there were none.

Rather, Rodgers flew by the "poor man's IFR" method: "I Follow Roads." When highways were missing he pursued the way west along railroad tracks, to become known to a future generation of gypsy pilots as the "Iron Beams." His plane was called the *Vin Fiz* after a new soft drink being introduced by his financial sponsor, Armour & Company (Fig. 1-1).

Designated the Wright Model EX, the *Vin Fiz* actually never reached the West Coast—except for the vertical rudder and the engine's drip pan. She had crashed 15 times in 68 landings and had been repeatedly rebuilt completely by mechanics who followed in a special train carrying spare parts.

The journey was not without danger. Flying across the Salton Sea in southern California, one eye on the piece of string and the other on the railroad tracks, Rodgers was startled by a thunderous explosion and severe vibration. A connecting rod had broken and rammed through the crankcase. Steel splinters pierced his body, and his goggles were covered with oil. Blinded, he managed to land safely and press on.

The following day Rodgers faced the supreme test. Headwinds of 60 mph were blowing off the Los Angeles Basin through San Gorgonio Pass, and the Model EX couldn't fly that fast. However, he stuck a fresh cigar in his mouth, climbed aboard the *Vin Fiz*, and took off. He climbed slowly higher and higher to more than a mile above the ground, then shoved the nose down and dove through the turbulence.

This time the radiator sprung a leak and sprayed Rodgers with scalding water, yet he gritted his teeth into the tearing wind and came through. A prize of $25,000, put up by publisher William Randolph Hearst for the first flight coast-to-coast in under 30 days, vanished. The trip had taken 49 days, but Rodgers was hailed as a hero.

His contribution to aviation was a recommendation that pilots should fly high, not low, like the Wright Brothers had recommended when they taught

Fig. 1-1. Cal Rodgers' Vin Fiz.

him to fly. You had more altitude from which to find an emergency field when your engine quit. He also recommended that the pilot be protected from the gale-force winds in flight by some sort of windscreen, and the cockpit was born.

In later years other pilots, like Rodgers, enjoyed cigar-smoking while flying, and among airmail pilots, the cigar became the second most common "instrument." It took a full cigar to fly 40 miles (in one hour) or two cigars to fly 80 miles.

Not all of the early birdmen used string or cigars, however; the noted French aviation pioneer Louis Bleriot did not carry a single instrument when he became the first man to fly an airplane across the English Channel in 1909 in his little shoulder-wing Bleriot monoplane. He did, however, carry a pair of crutches, which he need to ambulate after an earlier accident.

As early "aeroplanes" grew larger and faster, more and more instrumentation was necessary to assist the pilot in navigating across the land. In 1912, Victor Lougheed, a founding member of the Society of Automobile Engineers, would write in his *Aeroplane Designing For Amateurs*: "Aeroplane development can scarcely be said as yet to have progressed to the point of providing the air navigator with as completely formulated rules for keeping his course, and as efficient adjuncts and devices for air navigation, as have been developed for the mariner by centuries of water navigation, yet much good work in this direction has been done, and more is under way."

First Aero Charts

Lougheed observed that special maps of the earth's surface already were being prepared for airmen, "the best of these maps printed in colors simulating the actual appearance of the ground as it is seen from above, roads being white, forests green, water surfaces blue, etc. For convenience of handling, maps in the form of long, narrow bands, mounted on rollers that can be fed by hand as the country is traversed, are most favored by the European military officers experienced in cross-country flying."

Today's excellent aeronautical charts, published by the National Oceanic and Atmospheric Administration's National Ocean Survey of the U.S. Department of Commerce, are direct descendants of those early multicolored charts, with a difference: the colors are used primarily to designate elevations, from green at sea level to dark brown above 9000 feet. In addition, Radio Aids to Navigation and Communication boxes appear on today's charts largely in blue, along with a host of other information for the pilot covering airports, Airport Traffic Service, and Airspace Information, etc.

Lougheed was aware of another problem all pilots face today in following a desired track across the terrain—that of the need for a WCA (Wind Correction Angle) to be added to or subtracted from a magnetic heading to make good the planned course, sometimes called the "crab angle."

He said, "The disturbing influence of crosswinds, occasioning leeway so great as to carry a machine dozens of degrees out of its course in spite of its being kept constantly pointed in the desired direction, is a condition that does not prevail in water navigation, in which drifts due to the greatest and most rapid ocean currents are so slight as to require only very small allowances to be made for them."

If compass navigation presented fresh problems to the airmen of 1912, there was still another matter that made air navigation different from water navigation. The airplane travels in *three* dimensions, not two. Hence, a means of determining altitude accurately was early recognized as highly important, and the answer was to use a common weather barometer.

"A barometer carried on an aerial vehicle," said Lougheed, "serves two purposes—of indicating altitude and of forecasting weather changes. In either case, the barometer is simply a pressure gauge, showing the atmospheric pressure at any given time.

"In aneroid barometers, the air pressure is indicated by the action of the pressure against the thin metal sides of one or more flat vacuum chambers, made of thin, elastic, metal discs, between which springs are placed to resist the pressure. A simple multiplying device converts the very slight movement of the vacuum-cell walls into the more ample movement of a hand around a circular dial or across a recording surface."

Recording Barometers

The latter were *recording barometers* of the type used to verify world record flight attempts of the kind made by Arch Hoxsey in December, 1910, at Dominguez Field near Los Angeles, in an effort to return to America the world altitude record held by a French airman, Georges Legagneaux. Time and again Hoxsey climbed his Wright biplane into the sky over Los Angeles, at one time reaching a record altitude of 11,474 feet, more than two miles high. The flight was disqualified, however, when the representative of the Aero Club of America, Professor Harry La Verne Twining, discovered the barometer contained the wrong kind of graph paper (Fig. 1-2).

On December 30, Hoxsey reached an altitude of 10,575 feet, nearly a thousand feet lower than the prior flight, but still high enough to qualify as a record. Twining told Hoxsey, "It looks good, Arch, but the *Federation Aeronautique Internationale* in Paris will

Fig. 1-2. *Professor Twining examines Arch Hoxsey's barograph.*

demand proof that the barograph has been recalibrated properly before they let you bring the record back from France!"

On the last day of the year, Hoxsey faced a decision. What if the barograph *was* in error? He had one more chance, during the last day of the International Air Meet at Dominguez Field, to repeat his performance and sew up the record.

A howling Santa Ana wind was blowing, but he cast an eye skyward, set his jaw, and climbed into his ship. Seething coils of brown sand lashed across the field. At that moment his mechanic, Al Hazard, ran up and handed him a note from the press box. Only hours earlier, another birdman, John Moisant, had crashed to his death near New Orleans.

"Don't risk it, Arch!" Hazard pleaded.

Hoxsey laughed. "I'll live forever, Al! Gimme a prop!"

Hazard pulled the propeller blade through and the engine barked to life. In a moment he was off.

Another airshow pilot, Hubert Latham, had just landed. He shook his head as he watched Hoxsey disappear into the darkening sky. "That air is like Swiss cheese!" he shuddered.

High overhead, Arch Hoxsey's ship bounced crazily through the turbulent "air pockets" airmen of his day suspected were like potholes in the sky. All

other flying stopped and every eye was on Hoxsey's little Wright Flyer. The crowd was strangely silent, as if everyone were praying for his safety.

Hoxsey had barely reached 7000 feet when the blowing Santa Ana winds and a badly overheating engine forced him to stop climbing. Then a cry rang out: "Here he comes! In his Dive of Death!"

It was a favorite stunt Hoxsey used, to plunge down vertically from the high sky, headed for certain death until, at the last moment, he'd pull up. This time Hoxsey plunged down, down, down, a diving eagle, until at 600 feet swirling dust obscured him. Then his ship was seen to lurch suddenly through a half roll and whip into a two-turn spin.

Hoxsey's Wright Flyer struck earth directly in front of the crowded grandstand with a sickening crunch of splintering wood. A groan of anguish came from the thousands of spectators, as the pilot was thrown forward, spread-eagled into the dirt. The engine tore loose, crushing down on top of his body. The blood-thirsty crowd suddenly rushed from the stands to recover pieces of the wreckage for souvenirs. Hazard was ready for them. He grabbed a piece of broken strut and flailed it into the crowd.

Professor Twining pushed through the crowd and recovered the smashed barograph, which had peaked at 7142 feet altitude. He shook his head. Now

4

the barograph could not be used to recalibrate Hoxsey's earlier record flight. Hoxsey had gambled and lost, and to this day the FAI still denies him a place in aviation's Hall of Fame, one he gave his life to earn.

If those early days were wild ones, today's skies are safer because of their spirit of enthusiasm and daring to try out new ideas to make flying safer for everybody. But aviation had a long way to go to reach maturity in 1979 when the FAA reported a total of 814,667 licensed pilots, including 51,733 women.

Only a handful of pilots existed in America in 1911. The prestigious Aero Club of America that year listed only 26 licensed members, three of them deceased—Hoxsey, Ralph Johnstone, and John B. Moisant. By October, 1916, a list of 817 civilian aviators was published by the periodical *Aviation & Aeronautical Engineering*.

The general attitude toward flying machines was aptly expressed in October, 1910, by former President Theodore Roosevelt, who attended a performance by the Wright Exhibition Team at St. Louis and saw his first aircraft.

"Is this thing safe?" he bluntly asked Hoxsey, then one of the star performers.

"I'd certainly like to have you as a passenger, Colonel!" Hoxsey exclaimed. What better way to win confidence in airplanes than to take an ex-President for a spin?

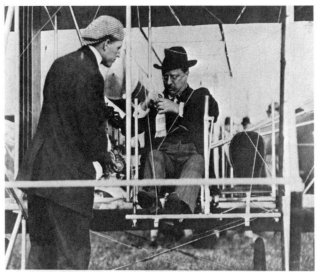

Fig. 1-3. Teddy Roosevelt flies with Arch Hoxsey.

Teddy climbed into the bucket seat on Hoxsey's right and clung anxiously to a wing strut as the Wright Flyer bumped over the turf (Fig. 1-3). There were no seat belts, no cockpit whatsoever. Hoxsey circled the field and dove low over the grandstand, while Roosevelt leaned out and waved. Hoxsey grabbed him by the belt and yanked him back into his seat.

Back on the ground Roosevelt climbed out, flashed his toothy grin and cried "First rate, young man! *Bully!*"

Chapter 2
The
Business Office

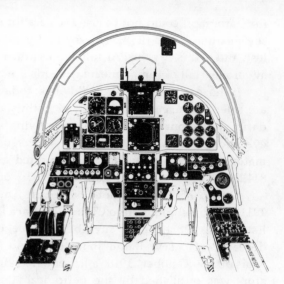

Military demands on precision aircraft performance during the First World War produced a number of radical changes in cockpit design, particularly in the instrumentation used for navigation during daytime and nighttime operations. It became clear that the cockpit was the heart of the aircraft, the life center where the man/machine was coordinated into a well-functioning entity.

In 1916, Lawrence Sperry of the Sperry Gyroscope Company conducted experiments in night flight at Amityville, Long Island, New York, combining the benefits of the Sperry automatic pilot, synchronized drift indicator, air compass, and a "lighting outfit." A battery of three 50-candlepower searchlights was mounted in the top leading edge of a biplane flying boat, with parabolic reflectors capable of increasing the candlepower to 40,000 for each lamp, to be used for night landings or for Morse code message sending.

At the same time, night lights were considered a hazard by airmen flying patrol missions hunting Zeppelins over England. Lieutenant Phil Radar, a Curtiss Company pilot who flew a number of such missions, reported: "As I was a night pilot in England on Zeppelin duty for six months, I have a good idea as to what is needed in a satisfactory illuminant for instruments. Electric lights were never satisfactory owing to the fact that they either cast such a blinding glare that you could see nothing else, or they were continually going out due to engine vibration. We always carried a hand flash lamp for emergency, and the only instrument that had luminous paint on it was our compass."

Much experimentation was done under the pressure of war to develop better luminous paint for instruments. One form of so-called "daylight paint" was made by roasting oyster shells with sulphur with the addition of other substances such as bismuth. A

better luminous paint consisted of phosphorescent zinc sulphide combined with radium, which had a half-life of 1700 years and so was able to last at least five years.

A.G. Hamlin, of the Radium Luminous Corporation, said in 1916: "Luminous compasses already have proven their worth in aviation, and it is hoped that the next few steps necessary for the full equipment of the instrument board will be taken without loss of time. The oil gauge, the aneroid, the inclinometer, barometer, ammeter, all can be treated with the new illuminant."

Standard Gauges Sought

Standardization of aircraft instruments was the goal of a special report issued by the National Advisory Committee for Aeronautics (NACA) in 1916 that stated: "All indicating instruments required in the navigation of aircraft should be as compact, rugged, and light as is consistent with accuracy, reliability, and durability, and with ease of reading." The NACA report specified that "barometers or altimeters must be sensitive and of open scale, and the lag in their operation should be the absolute minimum obtainable. When operating in a fog, it is essential that the distance above the surface should be known within very close limits."

Magnetic compasses, said NACA, should be so installed that they would be remote from the influence of magnetic materials in moving parts, such as control columns.

"Air speed meters," said NACA "should indicate reliably the speed through the air and should be free from the effects of acceleration, as when the machine is banking strongly in a turn, the effect of gravitation is augmented by the presence of centrifugal force."

Inclinometers of the pendulum or spirit-level type, said NACA, "are inaccurate in the presence of accelerations and are only useful as a general check as to the attitude of the machine when flying in a fog." A gyroscopic base line was suggested as the way to go, and today we have them in what is called the "attitude indicator" or "gyro horizon."

In place of today's turn and slip indicator, sometimes called the "ball-bank" indicator, NACA in 1916 pointed out that warplanes then used two types of sideslip indicators, "the simplest form being that of the well-known string or pennant, but the latter cannot be used satisfactorily in the wake of a tractor propeller. The other type consists of a very sensitive pendulum which indicates whether or not lateral accelerations are present, as will be the case for a machine which is not properly balanced laterally, but such an instrument is subject to the defect that if the machine is side-slipping laterally at a constant speed, lateral acceleration is no longer present." Today's turn and slip indicator actually is far simpler. The slip indicator is merely a liquid-filler curved glass tube containing an agate or steel ball, similar to a carpenter's level, while the turn part of the instrument uses gyroscopic precession to indicate the direction and rate of turn of the aircraft.

Airspeed indicators of 1916 were tested at the Massachusetts Institute of Technology in a wind tunnel whose maximum velocity was only 42 miles an hour. Said a Navy investigator, "On the other hand about 40 miles an hour is a common stalling speed for most airplanes and for that reason tests over this range are most valuable, and good airspeed meters should be reliable at these low speeds." (Today's pilots are aware that the *reverse* is often true—that at low airspeeds the indicators may be far off, largely due to the inclination of the pitot tube above the relative airflow in a stalling attitude.)

A curious suggestion was made by the Navy researcher in regard to airspeed meter readouts: "To correct for errors due to the decreasing density of the air at higher altitudes, it would seem desirable to have at least two speed scales on all gauges, one calibrated for sea level density, and the other corrected so that it will give the correct speed at some fixed altitude. With these two scales, the aviator could interpolate mentally with sufficient precision for practical purposes." Pilots today, of course, use a single airspeed scale, and mentally correct the IAS (Indicated Air Speed) for TAS (True Air Speed) either with a computer, adjusting for DA (Density Altitude) error, or by a rule-of-thumb guesstimate of an error of about 2 percent per 1000 feet altitude.

If World War I served as a proving ground for aircraft instrumentation, the postwar period brought new problems such as how to accommodate passengers. In the words of World War I Liberty engine developer Jesse G. Vincent, "I am very much afraid that the future of aeronautics is going to be jeopardized by a wholesale attempt to use the war machines, which are now available, for air transport work. These machines have been built strictly for fighting and bombing purposes, and while some of the larger day-and-night bombers can be adapted to certain kinds of commercial use, they will never be ideal."

Glenn L. Martin considered a "twin-engined, two-ton capacity, high-speed airplane the most important vehicle of the air in commercial service, because of its added reliability, due to the fact that one engine will fly and climb the machine with its two-ton useful load, and is capable of handling bad weather to a much greater degree than the smaller types." Martin, of course, was in the bomber business, hence his views may be considered a bit prejudiced, but he did agree that "a most important and valuable application not yet encouraged in this country is the carrying of passengers. Important centers located such places as Philadelphia and New York should have a ten or twelve-passenger machine leaving a well-equipped airdrome in both cities every half hour, and making the journey less than half the time consumed by other means of travel."

On the other hand, W.T. Thomas, president of the Thomas-Morse Aircraft Corporation, said, "I believe there is a market for low-priced aircraft for civilian flyers; but here again a great deal of press propaganda is needed to educate the public sufficiently to assure a sale of enough machines to allow their manufacture at a low price."

As things turned out, hundreds of JN4D Curtiss "Jenny" war trainers went onto the surplus market and were grabbed up at some $600 apiece, brand new, to form a fleet of gypsy flyers who barnstormed the nation in the 1920s and brought flying to America's grass roots.

Little by little, aviation grew up in the postwar years, and pilots learned more and more about how to use the instruments available in their cockpits for all-weather flying. It was all well and good for Charles Lindbergh to join the Caterpillar Club several times, bailing out of his airmail plane when trapped on top of a solid cloud deck rather than attempt an instrument letdown. "Lucky Lindy" lived to become a national hero by spanning the Atlantic solo in his *Spirit of St. Louis* in 1927.

Attitude Flying

But other airmen were training themselves to fly on the gauges and to feel completely at home in their cockpits come rain, storm, blizzard, or whatever. The transition from VFR (Visual Flight Rules) flying to IFR (Instrument Flight Rules) flying was first achieved when pilots learned to substitute their instruments for outside references in maintaining control of their aircraft—*Attitude Instrument Flying*. Such flying is described today by the FAA as "A means of controlling the attitude of the aircraft through reference to flight instruments."

In fact, some pilots have learned to include engine instruments in IFR flying. I recall one harrowing experience when my pitot tube iced up flying over the Wyoming country and my airspeed indicator went out. Next, the artificial horizon went out, also due to icing, so I kept a *sharp* eye on my engine's tachometer and listened to the change in pitch if the nose of my Cessna 180 lifted too high. A softening of the controls also warned of an approaching stall.

Switching from "primary" to "secondary" instruments in an emergency is important, but such "backup" instruments also are used supportively in IFR flying. Says the FAA: "Attitude instrument flying is like visual flying in that both use reference points to determine the attitude of the aircraft. While flying by visual reference to the earth's surface, the pilot determines the attitude of the aircraft by observing the relation between the nose and wings of the aircraft and natural horizon. While flying by reference to flight instruments, he determines the attitude of the aircraft by observing indications on the instruments which give him essentially the same information that he gets by reference to the earth's surface. Another similarity between attitude instrument flying and visual flying is the way in which the aircraft is controlled. Exactly the same control techniques are used while flying by reference to instruments as are used in visual flying."

Aside from attitude control of an aircraft, the pilot's biggest concern today is in the areas of navigation (flying from A to B) and communications (keeping in touch with Air Traffic Control, Flight Service Stations, control towers, etc.). In our crowded skies, aircraft must navigate through controlled airspace precisely, at specific altitudes, along aerial flyways marked by radio beacons and other electronic devices.

When Lindbergh crossed the Atlantic, on the other hand, he decided to fly without radio in order to save 90 pounds which he could better use carrying more fuel. He even ordered the fuel gauges left out to save more weight and kept track of fuel consumption with watch and tachometer.

Today, many aircraft have fuel-flow meters in their cockpits that assist in determining how much fuel the engines are burning, and at critical times careful pilots avoid using simple float-type fuel gauges, which may give erroneous readings. A pilot may run out one wing tank, listening for the engine to sputter before switching over to the other wing tank, but passengers do not like the sound of a sputtering engine, hence this practice is not often followed. Fuel mismanagement, incidentally, is one of the most frequent causes of accidents, where the pilot encounters headwinds and finds himself far from his destination with the fuel gauge needles in the red. At such times, a careful airman may elect to make a "precautionary" landing, maybe on a road with no traffic, near a gas station. Better, however, he should do his homework more carefully during the preflight period, check the Weather Bureau for upper winds en route, and otherwise avoid such pitfalls. Today, pilots can even check en route weather by calling up Flight Watch stations on 122.0, also known as Enroute Flight Advisory Service, to determine whether conditions have changed since their departure from the airport.

Emergency Frequency

Wise pilots also frequently monitor the emergency frequency 122.5, listening for any calls from a pilot in trouble. Emergency Locator Transmitters that go off automatically on that frequency may lead to a downed aircraft, but more often an ELT may have gone off accidentally, a source of concern for the FAA. Nevertheless, ELTs have saved lives.

A friend of mine was flying a seaplane Cessna 180 over the North Woods country of Canada when his engine iced up and he was forced to land in treetops short of a lake he had hoped to reach by stretching his deadstick glide. It didn't work. In freezing cold he remained in the cockpit of his aircraft, his ELT transmitting its WOW! WOW! WOW! message of distress. High overhead, a passing airline pilot monitoring the emergency frequency heard the distress call, verified the rough position where it was coming from, and called out the Royal Canadian Air Force searchers. Within hours they had dispatched a huge "flying crane" helicopter and yanked the 180 out of the treetops, carrying it to safety at a considerable expense to the pilot, who vowed never to be caught in such a situation again.

What could he have done? When all else fails, some pilots have cleared ice from their frozen carburetor intake manifolds by switching the ignition key on and off, causing a backfire. It's not highly recommended, though, as it could easily cause a disastrous engine fire. Better the pilot should have planned his flight to be *always* within gliding distance of a body of water in case just an emergency occurred. My friend now flies that way religiously.

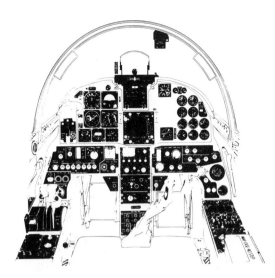

Chapter 3

Blind Man's Bluff

Early barnstormers who flew by the "seat of their pants" had little use for instrument flying for two reasons. First, they didn't understand the finer points of the technique, and second, there was little glamor in it for them. Wearing leather helmets and goggles, they roared across the skies in open cockpit biplanes, glancing at a silk stocking tied to a wing strut by a fair damsel to gauge the attitude of their plane, the same way pilots had flown since Wilbur and Orville Wright got their act together in 1903. There was the sound of the wind in the wires . . . the caress of breeze on their faces . . . the deep muscular sense of balance in the seats of their pants, actually a phenomenon known today as *kinesthesis*.

On a clear day they flew well this way, but in the event they were forced to descend through a low-lying fog bank, they were in deep trouble. Without visual clues to their plane's attitude, they were really flying blind and might be upside down or stalling without knowing it until too late.

Back in 1910, Elmer A. Sperry, president of the Sperry Gyroscope Company, had founded a business based on the principle of a child's spinning top. Such an object, according to laws of inertia, resists any change in direction of the spin axis. Sperry had applied the principle to the design of a successful stabilizer for ocean vessels and soon had adapted it to flying machines.

First Autopilot

He developed a practical bank-and-turn indicator, a gyrocompass, artificial horizon, and finally an automatic pilot, in which a gyroscopic device was linked to the flight controls to maintain the aircraft in a preset attitude in relation to the earth's horizon. He even developed a gyrostabilized bomb that could be interconnected to a computer, but bombers of the First World War could not fly high enough or fast enough to require such a device. Later, an employee

of the Sperry company perfected a gyroscopically stabilized bombsight. His name was Carl Norden.

Elmer Sperry's son, Lawrence, had learned to fly in order to carry out experimental tests of his father's inventions, and in the early twenties he began flight tests of blind flight techniques over Long Island. This led to the design of a small plane, the Sperry Messenger, and formation of the Lawrence Sperry Aircraft Company at Farmingdale, New York, to produce it.

On a sales trip to Europe, Lawrence Sperry made a number of demonstration flights in the Messenger, and one day in 1923 he attempted a flight across the English Channel. He didn't make it. Forced down near the French coast, he tried to swim to shore, but drowned. His father, Elmer, retired with a broken heart but soon regained his interest in life when a young pilot named James H. (Jimmy) Doolittle, an ex-Air Corps speed flyer who had won the Schneider Trophy Race in 1925, dropped by for a visit (Figs. 3-1, 3-2). Doolittle had earned his Doctorate in Aeronautical Engineering at Massachusetts Institute of Technology in a postgraduate course, and, like Sperry, had developed a keen interest in the problems of blind flying.

What Doolittle wanted was a special kind of instrument that would instantaneously tell him his direction of flight, without recourse to an electronic radio beam and its confusing *dit-dah* and *dah-dit* signals. Sperry sparked to the idea, went to work, and developed a combination artificial horizon and directional gyro, plus radio direction finder with vibrating hairlines on the dial to visually indicate where the radio beam lay, rather than aurally.

Next, Doolittle looked up a young engineer named Bernard Kollsman, who had developed in his garage a remarkably accurate barometric altimeter that could measure height above the ground within a few feet. Doolittle wanted these precision instru-

Fig. 3-1. Jimmy Doolittle won the 1931 Bendix Race in a Laird Super Solution with blind flying instruments.

ments for a good reason. The Air Corps had loaned him to Harry Guggenheim, president of the Daniel Guggenheim Foundation for the Promotion of Aeronautics, for special research work in blind flight.

Doolittle was assigned to head up the Guggenheim Full Flight Laboratory at Mitchel Field, Long Island, to develop an entirely new technique of blind flying. That he accomplished this within one year was a miracle of modern flying and engineering. The problem was this: by using rudimentary flight instruments such as the magnetic compass, altimeter, and airspeed indicator, along with Sperry's needle-and-ball device, pilots could manage to keep their aircraft from going into a spin inadvertently, yet there were no instruments until then to use in navigating through dense fogs.

As an Air Service Lieutenant, Doolittle in 1922 had flown a DH-4 biplane coast to coast, from Pablo Beach, Florida, to Rockwell Field, San Diego, stopping for gas at Kelly Field in Texas. It was a time of keen competition between the Army and Navy, and Jimmy was under pressure to bring off a good flight. Doolittle had never even seen a Sperry Turn Indicator, so the first thing he did was fly up to McCook Field in Ohio and scrounge one from a friend in the engineering office.

At Mitchel Field, Doolittle persuaded one of his former teachers at MIT, Professor William G. Brown, to join his project as an instrument expert. Lieutenant Benjamin Kelsey was assigned as his flight assistant

Fig. 3-2. Instrument panel of Jimmy Doolittle's 1931 Bendix Race Super Solution.

for the historic tests to be made in a Consolidated NY-2 "Husky" biplane that had two cockpits, the rear one covered with a canvas hood to shut out all visual cues except those provided by the instrumented cockpit panel (Fig. 3-3).

A Hair-Raiser

Doolittle's experience with the scrounged Sperry Turn Indicator at McCook Field would give him confidence in the Mitchel Field tests, for the earlier event had been a real hair-raiser. During an interview, Doolittle related to me what happened: "I took off just after dark, having chosen a moonlight night to facilitate night flying, but after four hours out I ran into a solid overcast and then severe thunderstorms. For a while the lightning flashes were almost constant and, in the otherwise black night, so intense as to light up the ground clearly for a considerable area. Some flashes were so close that their familiar ozone odor could be detected, but although it seemed that one could reach out and touch them, none struck the plane.

"The air was extremely turbulent and the airplane was violently thrown about its axes as well as

up and down and, despite its excellent stability characteristics, was held on a relatively even keel only with great concentration and effort. After the lightning died away the turbulence appeared to intensify, and there was about an hour in the jet black darkness when no ground reference point could be seen, and it would have been quite impossible to maintain proper attitude and course without the blessed bank and turn indicator. Although I had been flying for almost five years by the 'seat of my pants,' and considered that I had achieved some skill at it, that particular flight made me a firm believer in proper instrumentation for bad weather flying!"

Curiously, the Army Air Service in the 1920s still paid much attention to the mythical "flying instinct" of seat-of-the-pants pilotage and devised a number of tests to determine whether a cadet possessed this rare, birdlike quality. One was the Jones-Barany revolving chair, in which the student was spun round and round to check on his "nystagmus," a rapid and involuntary side-to-side eye movement.

In 1926 Capt. David A. Myers, an Army flight surgeon, augmented this test by having the pilot close his eyes while being spun around. It was found that if he was slowed down and gently stopped, he had the sensation of spinning in the opposite direction. This occurred because we normally maintain equilibrium by use of sight, touch, hearing, kinesthetic (muscular) and vestibular senses. Touch and hearing are not important in flight orientation, Doolittle explained to me, and with the loss of sight, the most reliable of the remaining senses, we get our sense of balance from the deep-muscular nerves and from the fluid movement sensors in the vestibular canals of our ears.

"Instinct" a Myth

In 1926 another brilliant Air Corps research pilot, Capt. William C. Ocker, took Capt. Myers' new blindfold test and flunked it. Here, he knew, was positive proof that a flyer's "instinct" in fact did not

Fig. 3-3. Consolidated NY-2 Husky flown by Doolittle.

exist. No pilot could consistently fly blind without proper instruments. He thereafter carried with him on all flights a portable bank-and-turn indicator, complete with a venturi to drive it. Installing this device inside a lightproof "black box" Jones-Barany chair, he began training pilots to disregard their own senses and believe fully in their instruments. It was the forerunner of today's flight simulator.

It was back at this time that Jimmy Doolittle, then chief test pilot at McCooks Field, set out to learn whether he could expand his own skills in weather flying simply by memorizing landmarks on low-level cross-country runs in weather that ducks wouldn't fly in.

"I knew every high building, tree, silo, radio tower and high-tension line in the area," he said. "I could therefore fly in—or under—adverse weather safely when other equally experienced pilots did not fly. It was not that I was a better or more daring pilot. Constant practice simply extended my limitations. The trick was to learn them and not go beyond them. I thought that I was being smart, but the commanding officer, learning that I frequently flew in that area when other pilots did not, thought differently. He removed me from the job of chief pilot as he was totally unaware of my training program, advising me that I did not have judgment enough to be a pilot, and assigned me to the airplane section as an aeronautical engineer."

The effort was not in vain, however, for the Guggenheim people heard about his weather flying and sent for him to set up their Full Flight Laboratory. They couldn't have chosen a better qualified pilot. Doolittle's first step in the project was to look up Elmer Sperry, Sr., and sketch on the back of an envelope a rough picture of a new instrument he believed could be used to hold a steady course on a final approach to a blind landing.

Long evening bull sessions were spent discussing how best to design and utilize the Sperry artificial horizon and directional gyroscope, but not until he actually tried them out did he realize how effective they were. Gone forever was reliance on "pilot instinct." Now he had actual extensions of his eyes to tell him when he might stray off course, or get a wing down.

Doolittle recalled how Bill Ocker used to lecture on why it was important to rely on gyro turn indicators instead of a magnetic compass. It was better, he told his cadets, to carry two magnetic compasses, because of their inherent unreliability. When a cadet asked how he knew which compass was right if both gave different readings, Ocker grinned. "Well, maybe you should carry *three!*"

First DG

The DG (directional gyro) that Elmer Sperry, Jr., finally developed for Doolittle had no knob with which to reset it when it "precessed" or drifted off heading; instead it had a removable face. Doolittle recalled, "You released two springs, took the face off, stuck your finger in and turned it to where you wanted it, then started it up again. It wasn't exactly satisfactory, but remember, it was the first one."

When Doolittle checked out Bernard Kollsman's new sensitive altimeter, it was not even installed in the aircraft. Kollsman simply climbed into a Guggenheim plane and held the instrument on his lap. A second sensitive altimeter on the ground was used to calibrate the one in the air, to insure that both read the same during normal diurnal atmospheric pressure changes. The two were coordinated by radio.

With the instrumentation of the Consolidated NY-2 biplane completed for checking attitude and altitude, a way had to be found to verify his position in relation to the home base at Mitchel Field. The system chosen was adopted only after exhaustive studies of other ideas, such as the leader cable system being tried out in France and England. With it, the pilot simply followed the electromagnetic field of a ground cable stretched across the ground in wide ellipse, from takeoff to landing. Another idea tried out in England utilized captive balloons tethered to float above a fogbank. A fancy landing aid studied and discarded consisted of a mechanical sensor that hung below the aircraft and alerted the pilot when it struck the ground.

While the flight instruments were being perfected at the Full Flight Laboratory, work was pressed in development of the radio-beacon concept to assist the pilot in locating the field. With the help of the National Bureau of Standards and the Department of Commerce, the Laboratory developed a short-range, visual type 290 kilocycle radio beacon to use along with a standard Army type radio range beacon placed at the edge of the field. Inside the cockpit, Doolittle watched the instrument's two vibrating reeds to tell which side of the radio beam he was flying on. If he flew to the left, the left reed vibrated more rapidly than the right reed, and vice versa.

From 1928 into the summer of 1929 Doolittle made literally hundreds of blind landings and perfected his instrument flying. He scratched a mark on the throttle quadrant to achieve the identical manifold pressure on each approach. He carefully watched his airspeed indicator; at the proper power setting and airspeed, he always found the same rate of descent in calm air. With the hood over his cockpit he actually became more proficient at landing than during visual flight, with Lieutenant Kelsey riding the front seat looking out for other traffic. Now all they needed was a really foggy day to prove that the instrument landing system really worked. Jimmy was convinced that it would, but to prove it to others, there was only one way to fly—totally blind inside a fog bank.

Then on the dark and stormy night of March 15, 1929, the passengers aboard a southbound New York Central train were shocked to see a lumbering 02U-1 biplane swoop down out of nowhere and fly alongside them, the lower wingtip almost touching the car. For mile after mile, the train and plane hurtled down the Hudson River Valley together. Station after station flashed by—Catskill . . . Saugerties . . . Kingston. "My God," one passenger shouted, "he's gonna land on the train!"

Inside the cockpit of the rain-splattered ship the pilot had no such plan—he was merely flying the "iron beam" as only one pilot in the world could— Jimmy Doolittle. Wiping his goggles on his forearm, he slipped in still closer as darkness engulfed them. His eyes were intent on the lighted windows of the train glowing dimly through the rain. Suddenly the lights went out—the train was boring into a tunnel!

Doolittle abruptly pulled up, swung out over the Hudson River and groped his way along, searching for a place to land. Not too far distant, he knew, was the West Point parade ground. Once more he picked up the tracks on the west side of the river. The ground slowly began rising, and the parade ground was 167 feet above the river; soon Jimmy was engulfed again in cloud. Storm King Mountain was somewhere nearby. He zoomed away and dropped down to skim the waves.

Doolittle was deliberately flying through adverse weather to reaffirm what he had learned at McCook Field—that he could extend his limitations by memorizing the terrain. But would it work this time? In the distance, the Jersey Palisades loomed before him. He swung across the river, approaching Manhattan Island on the far side of the Hudson, somehow missing the East Pier of the New George Washington Bridge. He had decided to crash-land in Battery Park, but people were all over it, like so many ants. He pulled up and flew on.

He rejected the idea of continuing on to his intended destination, Mitchel Field, as he had no radio on board. He recalled: "It appeared that a crash landing in the river might be necessary, so I removed my parachute in order to be able to swim ashore. The water, on closer inspection, looked uninviting, so I decided on a final try—this time for Newark Airport."

Once again Doolittle, enveloped in swirling mists, headed for a region of power lines and radio towers that he could not see. He finally said to hell with it and pulled up through the 1000-foot layer of cloud. On top, the stars were clear, a moon rising in the east. He swung west, hoping the fog would dissipate over Pennsylvania before he ran out of gas.

Suddenly, down below, he spotted a revolving beacon light through a break in the undercast. He flipped on his landing lights, shoved the nose down and dove through the hole. Once again visibility dropped to zero, just as a giant oak loomed dead ahead. He swerved, but too late—a branch pierced the lower wing.

His engine sputtering, Doolittle circled, finally saw a black area ahead, and headed for it, but another tree blocked his way. He struck it, the ship swinging around, wrenching apart. He'd long ago decided that the best way to crash-land was to run into a treetop, letting a crumpling wing absorb the impact. He stepped out, unscathed.

"That flight," Doolittle told the author, "pointed up the importance of constant radio communications between aircraft and ground, and the need for frequent and accurate weather reports obtainable by radio during flight, in order to insure a safe continuation or to indicate suitable alternate destinations. It also indicated the desirability of a special light to mark emergency fields for night landings."

The Big Test

Back at Mitchel Field, Jimmy Doolittle knew he was ready for the big test—a fully blind flight from takeoff to landing, something never before achieved by any pilot. On September 24, 1929, the fog rolled in. In the predawn darkness, Jack Dalton, a Laboratory assistant looked outside. Mitchel Field was completely socked in. He picked up the phone and called Doolittle.

Before attempting a totally blind flight under actual weather conditions for the first time, the Laboratory researchers wanted to try out a unique fog dispersal system that had showed theoretical promise. As Doolittle told me "There was a chap in Cleveland who had a quarry. Instead of blasting rocks off the face of the quarry, he had a great blowtorch, about a foot in diameter and ten feet long. Unequal expansion and contraction caused the rock to fracture when he applied the heat.

"This chap, whose name was Reader, observed that on days when there was considerable ground fog, the heat of the device would dissipate the fog. He dropped us a note, saying he thought he had an idea for fog dissipation. We asked him to come to Mitchel Field with his gadget and stand by until we had a real dense fog situation and see if he could disperse it."

On that foggy morning in 1929, Reader joined the others at the Full Flight Laboratory. "We lit up his blowtorch," Jimmy recalled, "and it was true—it did disperse the fog in the immediate vicinity of the flame, but there was a slight breeze. New fog rolled in faster than it could be burned off."

FIDO

In later years, when General James H. Doolittle commanded the Eighth Air Force in England during World War II. FIDO [Fog Intensive, Dispersal Of] units similar to Reader's device did save many lives. Said Doolittle: "In England they did burn off great areas. When fog set in there, it frequently did so in a dead calm and became extremely dense. We saved many of our aircraft coming back from bombing Germany. They would have been lost without the several of those FIDO fields that we had."

On the big day of September, 1929, Doolittle recalled, "We had been making practice blind landings for a year and here was a chance to try our system out under actual operating conditions. Our airplane was rolled out, and I got aboard. Bill Brown manned the radio equipment on the ground, and a successful flight was accomplished."

Thus it was that Jimmy Doolittle tersely described how he made history that foggy morning, on a solo flight that had largely been forgotten, for a simple reason. Later that same morning he made a second "official" flight in the presence of Mr. Guggenheim, and gentleman that he was, he wanted full credit to go to the whole team effort.

He told it this way: "Just after landing, Mr. Guggenheim arrived and, as the fog was lifting, it was decided to give an official demonstration for him. I was completely enclosed in a covered cockpit so that I couldn't see anything outside the airplane and, with Lieutenant Kelsey as safety pilot, executed, by instruments alone, another takeoff, flight, and landing. This was the first instrument flight of record, but the real first flight was made alone in the fog."

On the Beam

The way he recalled it to me, "The first thing I did was taxi out until I got onto the radio beam, a two-kilowatt, semi-portable, two-legged range installed on the west side of Mitchel Field. I then turned the airplane until it was in the direction of the beam, made a normal takeoff, flew out for a set distance, made a 180-degree turn, flew back for a certain distance, made another 180-degree turn, lined up on the beacon on the edge of the field and on the landing beam, came in and passed over the landing beacon at the specified altitude.

"I then headed toward the beacon on the other side of the field and then, just gradually and carefully, at a prearranged and practiced rate of descent, rpm and airspeed, flew at a very gentle angle directly into the ground. The landing gear was able to accept the slight downward velocity. I'd been doing this for the better part of a year, and I'd come to make just as good or perhaps a *better* landing than I could when I looked. You gave yourself over completely to the instruments which, unlike the human animal, function the same every time."

Doolittle's pioneer work on instrument flying did not end with his assignment to the Guggenheim experiments. In 1930, on leaving the Air Corps, he joined Shell Oil Company and arranged with the Collins radio people to install special navigation equipment in his Lockheed Orion.

"I continued to fly under bad weather conditions and to memorize the routes," he remembered. "I would many times come into St. Louis, where I was stationed, and have the controller in the tower say: 'This field is closed—there is no landing here!' I'd say, 'This is Jimmy Doolittle!' and he'd say, 'All right, Jimmy, come on in!' "

Today, no longer need non-airline pilots grope their way under low scud, flying from landmark to landmark, as Jimmy Doolittle did back in the 1920s. As an outgrowth of the Guggenheim experiments half a century ago, more than 1000 VOR radio navigation stations in the United States provide 157,853 nautical miles of low-altitude VHF VOR/VORTAC airways, plus another 31,625 miles of alternate routes and 135,920 high-altitude jet routes.

The FAA's vast air routes also include 1015 NDBs (Non-Directional Beacons) for Automatic Direction Finding radio navigation; 25 Air Route Traffic Control Centers; 499 Airport Control Towers; 318 Flight Service Stations; 753 Instrument Landing Systems, and 192 Airport Surveillance Radars.

All these electronic services now provide pilots with true all-weather flying capability, providing their cockpits are properly equipped with receiving and sending equipment to keep in touch with ground controllers when nothing is visible outside the cockpit windows.

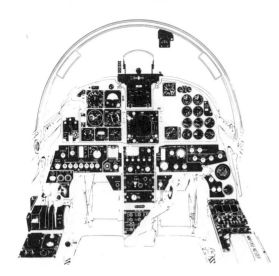

Chapter 4

Flight Instruments: How They Work

The basic flight instruments in the cockpit of your airplane can be your best friend, or, if you do not understand their function and inherent errors, your worst enemy. Flying in weather, there are times when you are completely dependent on their readings to know what is going on outside the cockpit, what your aircraft is up to, where it is, and where it is going. All flight instruments may be categorized as to the natural forces upon which they depend in operation—magnetism, air density and pressure, or gyroscopic forces.

Magnetic Compass

Of all the basic flight instruments, only one separates solely under "outside control"—the thing stuck up above the panel, close to the windshield, called the magnetic compass (Fig. 4-1). Electrical failure, icing, or other problems can disrupt the functions of all other instruments, yet the little mag compass keeps right on working, most of the time. But even it has inherent problems, some due to natural forces outside the aircraft, others due to installation error or other distractions within the cockpit.

Although it is the simplest and least precise instrument used to tell you which way you're headed, the magnetic compass, by and large, is considered the most reliable by generations of airmen. When all else fails, you can steer your course by using it, or if you suspect troubles in other direction indicators, you can use the magnetic compass to cross-check them.

Historically, magnetic compasses date back to the 12th Century A.D.; the earliest type of mariner's compass consisted of a magnetized needle thrust inside a reed and floated in a bowl of water. Oddly, the compass card is far older than the magnetic compass itself, and originally was known as the *rosa ventorum*, or wind rose, which carried eight principal points marked with the initials of the principal winds, dating back to Temple of the Winds in Athens, built by

Andronicus of Cyrrhus—*tramontana, greco, levanter, sirocco, ostro, africo, ponente,* and *maestro*. In Christopher Columbus' time, dry-card compasses were in common use, along with an hourglass hung from a beam so the sand could flow freely from its upper to lower half to measure elapsed time.

Today's panel-mounted magnetic compass still works on the same principles as those of the ancients—the south end of two steel bar magnets, mounted on a float around which the compass card is placed, always seek magnetic north. Modern compass cards are marked with letters for cardinal headings (N, S, E, W) and every 30 degrees is represented with a number, the last zero of which is omitted. Between these numbers the card is graduated for each 5 degrees.

The compass float assembly is housed in a bowl filled with acid-free white kerosene that dampens out excessive oscillations of the compass card, and at the same time provides lubrication for the pivot point and prevents rust. A rubber line is mounted behind the glass face, and at the rear of the compass is a rubber diaphragm to allow for expansion and contraction when flying at different altitudes.

It is reported that Columbus mounted the compass needles on his cards askew on his second voyage in 1783 to correct for magnetic variation—the angle between the way the compass points and the true meridian. In the year 1600, William Gilbert first proposed that the earth itself was a great magnet, but he believed that variation was caused by magnetic attraction of land masses. We now know, of course, that its cause is the displacement of the magnetic north pole from true north.

Compass Errors

An error different from *compass variation* is *compass deviation*, caused by anything in the aircraft that has a magnetic field and influences the iron bars in the

15

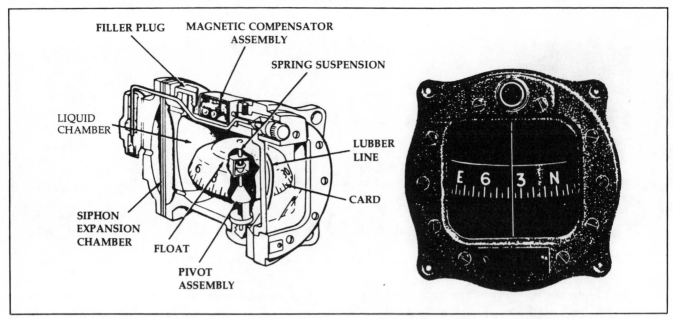

Fig. 4-1. Magnetic compass components. (courtesy FAA)

compass, such as the steel control column. Place a metal flashlight on the instrument panel next to the mag compass and watch it go crazy! Some radio equipment also can affect the mag compass reading, so it should be checked both with the radios on and off.

To correct for deviation error, the aircraft is placed on a compass rose painted on the airport ramp with cardinal lines radiating in predetermined accuracy (Fig. 4-2). With engine running and radios on to your favorite station, adjustment screws in the compass are turned to minimize these errors, a process called *swinging the compass*. After calibration, a *compass correction card* is filled out and posted near the compass to show the proper headings to steer, such as: *For N steer 005*.

Disregarding the fact the earth's north and south magnetic poles have reversed themselves hundreds of times over its long history, we must also concern ourselves with a phenomenon called *magnetic dip*. Magnetic needles tend to point downward in middle and high latitudes, aligning themselves more completely with the earth's magnetic lines of force (flux) as they dip downward to the surface at the poles. Dip induces fluctuating errors in your mag compass during acceleration or deceleration on east or west headings, or during turns through north and south. In compensating for northerly turning error (Fig. 4-3) for example, the pilot will normally roll out of the turn before he reaches his desired heading; compensating for the southerly turning error, he will turn past his heading, then roll out.

To avoid wrestling with such errors, however, the pilot need only establish a bank that will produce a rate of turn of, say, three degrees per second, hold the

turn needle deflected by one needle width for the desired time, then roll out (for a 30-degree turn, fly one needlewidth for ten seconds). With wings level, the compass will settle down, and if you're off a bit, a small correction puts you on course.

Reliable as the magnetic compass is, when properly flown, it can still give you the horrors, as it did me one time on a flight over the high prairie country of Wyoming, when I encountered IFR weather in a cold front and started to climb to a higher altitude for better radio reception in filing an IFR flight plan with the Air Route Traffic Control Center at Denver.

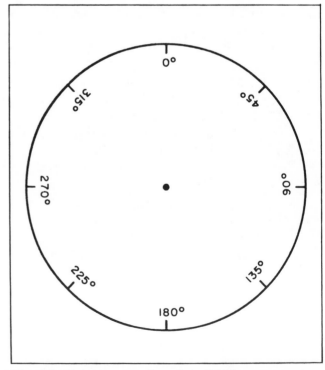

Fig. 4-2. Compass rose. (courtesy FAA)

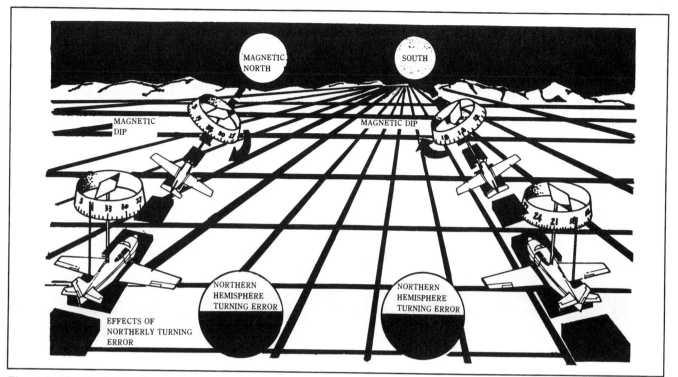

Fig. 4-3. Northerly turning error. (courtesy FAA)

First, my windshield iced over; next, the venturi iced up, making my gyros useless. I applied carburetor heat when the engine began sputtering from ice in the carb throat, but after all, I still had my old reliable magnetic compass—I thought! Suddenly I smelled kerosene. The rubber diaphram behind the mag compass had ruptured, and the card lay on its side, useless!

What to do? I listened to the sound of my engine, watching the rmps on the tachometer, and trimmed up for a steady climb until I broke free of cloud, sweatier but wiser.

Needle-Ball-Airspeed

Pilots who learn instrument techniques today using the attitude indicator as their prime reference are missing a lot of fun—flying basic IFR by "Needle-Ball-Airspeed," a technique drilled into maybe 100,000 pilots during the World War II years before we got all this fancy stuff in the cockpit. With those instruments alone you could waltz across the sky in perfect confidence that you knew which way you were flying, how fast you were turning, and whether you were in level flight, climbing, or diving. Skidding your turns? The ball told on you! Slipping? The ball never lied!

Today, we can still learn much from flying with needle-ball-airspeed as primary instruments for both control and performance, even though the "Turn and Slip Indicator" (Fig. 4-4) now serves only as a standby gadget due to the inherent reliability, simplicity, and effectiveness of our modern gyro attitude indicators.

The heart of the turn indicator is its gyroscope, or gyro, driven either by vacuum or electricity. Semirigid mounting of the gyro allows it to rotate freely about the lateral and longitudinal axes, while restricting its rotation about the vertical axis. The gyro axis is horizontally mounted so that the gyro rotates up and away from the pilot's position. The gimbal around the gyro is pivoted fore and aft.

Gyroscopic precession causes the rotor to tilt when the aircraft is turned. Due to the direction of rotation, the gyro assembly tilts in the opposite direction from that in which the aircraft is turning, preventing the

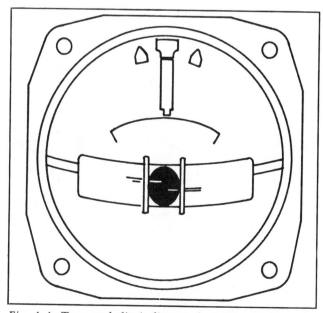

Fig. 4-4. Turn and slip indicator. (courtesy FAA)

17

rotor axis from becoming vertical to the earth's surface. The linkage between the gyro assembly and the turn needle, called the reversing mechanism, causes the needle to indicate the correct direction of turn.

A spring is attached between the instrument case and the gyro assembly to hold the gyro upright when no precession force is being applied. Spring tension may be adjusted to calibrate the instrument for a given rate of turn. The spring restricts the amount of gyro tilt, and stops the gyrp assembly from tilting more than 45 degrees to either side of the upright position. In addition, a damping mechanism prevents excessive oscillation of the turn needle.

Power to drive the electric gyro may be supplied from either an ac or dc source. When current is supplied directly from the battery, the needle gives reliable indications regardless of malfunction or failure of other components of the electrical system.

Power for the suction-driven turn needle is regulated by a restrictor valve installed between the main suction line and the instrument, to provide the correct amount of suction and rotor speed. For a specific rate of turn, low vacuum produces less-than-normal rotor speed and therefore less precession force. Needle deflection thus is less for this specific rate of turn, and the reverse is true when you have a high vacuum.

Using the Turn Needle

The turn needle indicates the rate of turn of the aircraft about its vertical axis in number of degrees per second, and if you learn to read it properly it will provide bank as well as rate-of-turn information, when you understand the relationship between airspeed, angle of bank, and rate of turn.

Earlier instruments are calibrated for a 2-minute-per-360-degree turn, and if accurately calibrated, a single needle-width deflection indicates a "standard rate" 3-degrees-per-second turn rate. On later 4-minute-turn models, one needle-width deflection indicates a rate of turn of 1½ degrees per second, or half the standard rate, primarily for use in higher-speed aircraft.

Another version is called the turn coordinator or pictorial turn indicator, in which the turn needle is replaced with a miniature airplane that responds to yaw and roll by banking, with the vertical tail serving as a "needle."

The vacuum system of gyro instruments spins the rotor by sucking a stream of air against the rotor vanes, like an old-fashioned water wheel. Air at atmospheric pressure enters the instrument through filters and is later vented back into the atmosphere. Either a venturi or a vacuum pump is used to provide the required suction to spin the rotors of the gyro instruments (Fig. 4-5).

A venturi tube is most common in light aircraft because of its low cost and simplicity of installation and operation. A venturi with a 2-inch vacuum capacity can operate the turn needle, but an additional

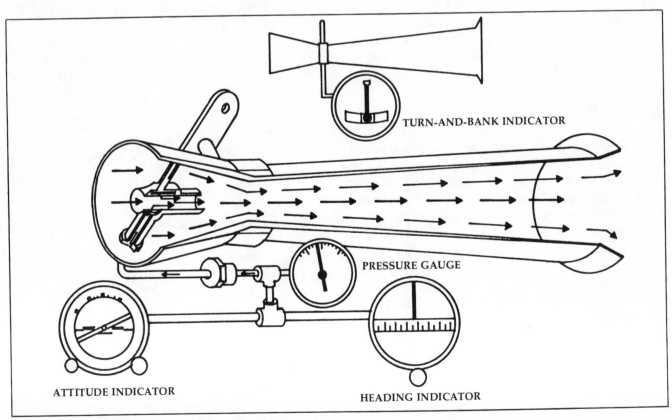

TURN-AND-BANK INDICATOR

PRESSURE GAUGE

ATTITUDE INDICATOR

HEADING INDICATOR

Fig. 4-5. Venturi vacuum system. (courtesy FAA)

8-inches is required to run attitude and heading indicators. The venturi is designed to operate at roughly 100 mph under standard sea level conditions, hence wide variations in airspeed or air density will affect the readings. Also, the rotor doesn't wind up to normal operating rpms until after takeoff, hence you can't make a preflight checkout of venturi-operated gyros. Icing in the venturi's throat also can play havoc, as I found out up in Wyoming country!

For these reasons, engine-driven vacuum pumps have become common in general aviation aircraft, usually mounted on the accessory driveshaft of the engine. Pump capacity and size vary according to how many gyros are to be operated.

Electrically-driven gyros were designed primarily for military operations because of erratic operation of vacuum-driven gyros at high altitudes. At 18,000 feet, where the air pressure is roughly half that at sea level, the vacuum pump becomes only half as efficient as at sea level. An electric gyro in light aircraft is a safety plus—in the event of a vacuum failure in attitude and heading indicators, the pilot can fall back on a turn needle operated by an electric gyro.

Attitude Indicators

The newer attitude gyro, or attitude indicator (Fig. 4-6), today is the prime instrument used in IFR flying, for good reason—it is the sole instrument that substitutes for the natural horizon and shows immediately whether the aircraft is flying straight and level, climbing, diving, or banking, and thus is normally mounted directly in front of the pilot(s).

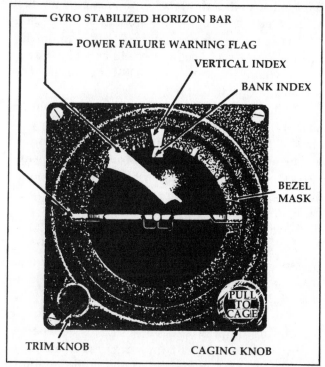

GYRO STABILIZED HORIZON BAR
POWER FAILURE WARNING FLAG
VERTICAL INDEX
BANK INDEX
BEZEL MASK
PULL TO CAGE
TRIM KNOB   CAGING KNOB

Fig. 4-6. Gyro horizon. (courtesy FAA)

The suction-driven attitude indicator developed during World War II permitted development of attitude instrument flying as we know it today. It was formerly known as the flight indicator. The first widely-used electric attitude indicator, the self-contained J-8, was originally designed for fighter aircaft, and permits 360-degree rolls and loops without causing the gyro to tumble. Roll inverted and the ball of this indicator quickly rotates through 180 degrees, through controlled precession. Other attitude indicators, or artificial horizons, that do not have this capability usually are caged by the pilot prior to executing aerobatic maneuvers, to prevent them from tumbling.

Most recent advances in instrument design have given us the Integrated Flight System, sometimes called the Flight Director System, which combines the gyro horizon with other instruments to cut down the number of instruments the pilots must watch when flying IFR.

An Integrated Flight System consists of electronic components that compute and indicate the aircraft attitude required to attain and maintain a pre-selected flight condition. Command indicators tell the pilot in which direction and by how much to change aircraft attitude to achieve the desired result. The computed command indications relieve the pilot of many mental calculations necessary for instruments flight.

A typical Integrated Flight System includes a control panel, a flight director indicator, (FDI) a course indicator, a steering computer, and an instrument and an instrument amplifier. The control panel contains the controls by which the pilot selects the desired mode of operation. When a mode is selected, the corresponding annunciator is illuminated on the periphery of the FDI. Today, flying under Category II weather conditions, a Flight Control Guidance, consisting of either an autopilot with an approach coupler or a Flight Director System, is required.

Many types of heading or directional indicators are in use today, the most common for light aircraft being the relatively simple directional gyro, or DG. The DG has no direction-seeking properties and must be set manually to the proper heading as indicated by the magnetic compass, with or without including variation or deviation errors.

A vacuum-driven DG powered by an engine-driven vacuum pump or venturi rotates at speeds of from 10,000 to 18,000 rpm, at pressures from 3.5 to 5.0 inches of mercury. The chief error of the DG is precession due to bearing friction, which causes the card to creep or drift, requiring resetting periodically. Other sources of precession error may be unbalanced gyro components and the effect of the earth's rotation, noticeable only during flights covering considerable changes in latitude. The FAA recommends checking the DG every 15 minutes at least, against the magnetic compass, though an error of 3 degrees or less is acceptable for normal operations. (Most pilots feel they're doing a good job holding to within 5 degrees of their desired heading).

A refinement of the old type DG is the Azimuth Directional Gyro (Fig. 4-7), in which the azimuth card is mounted on the face of the instrument and rotates as the aircraft turns. The aircraft's heading is shown under the pointer on the nose of the tiny aircraft on the instrument's glass face.

Remote Compasses

Remote Indicating Compasses have been developed to compensate for errors and reduce limitations of the older type heading indicators, but because of their size, weight, cost, and other factors, you don't find many in light planes, though more and more executive (business) aircraft are using them today. Advantages include lack of dip error because the instrument is gyro-stabilized, and no correction card, as deviation is almost fully compensated. Precession errors are minimal and constant resetting is not required.

The radio magnetic indicator (RMI) is another innovation for modern general aviation aircraft, consisting of a rotating compass card, a double-barred bearing indicator, and a single-barred bearing indicator (Fig. 4-8). The compass card, actuated by the aircraft's compass system, rotates as the aircraft turns. The magnetic heading of the aircraft is always directly under the index at the top of the instrument, assuming no deviation error.

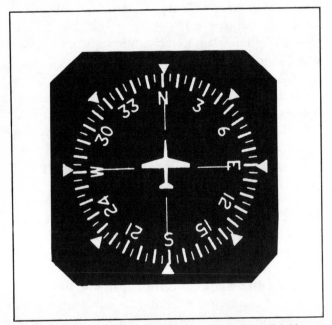

Fig. 4-7. Azimuth directional gyro. (courtesy FAA)

Fig. 4-8. King RMI indicator. (courtesy King)

The bearing pointers display ADF or VOR magnetic bearings to the selected station. In most installations, the double-barred bearing indicator gives the magnetic bearing to the VOR or VORTAC station to which the receiver is tuned, while the single-barred indicator is an ADF needle which gives the magnetic bearing to the selected low-frequency facility. The tail of the double-barrel indicator tells you your magnetic bearing from a low-frequency radio station.

Some RMIs have selector switches permitting the pilot to use both indicators in conjunction with dual VOR receivers, or both indicators as ADF needles. When used with area navigation (RNAV) equipment, the RMI can be set up to indicate either the bearing to the waypoint, or to the VOR/DME station used to establish the waypoint.

Of the six basic flight instruments used in either VFR or IFR flying, three we have mentioned are gyro-controlled—attitude indicator, heading indicator, and turn indicator—while the rest operate in response to pressures derived through what is called the pitot-static system—the pressure altimeter, airspeed indicator, and vertical-speed indicator.

Two types of pitot-static systems are available, both of which supply a source of static (atmospheric) pressure and impact (ram) air pressure to the various instruments. Their difference lies largely in the location of the static source (Fig. 4-9).

The more recently developed system provides for location of the pitot and static sources at separate positions on the aircraft. Impact pressure is taken from the pitot tube, mounted parallel to the longitudinal axis and generally in line with the relative wind,

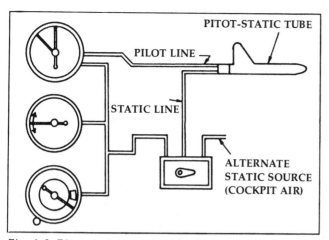

Fig. 4-9. Pitot-static system with alternate static pressure source. (courtesy FAA)

usually in the wing's leading edge, in the nose section, or vertical stabilizer, to be free from airflow disturbance. Some pitot heads (Fig. 4-10) are electrically heated to keep them free of ice.

Static pressure is taken from a static line attached to the pitot-static head or to a vent attached flush to the fuselage side or nose section. Some installations use two vents, one on each side of the fuselage, to compensate for any variation in static pressure due to slipping or skidding. Wise pilots keep the pitot mast covered when not in use to prevent bugs from crawling inside and blocking the tubes, which will leave you without an airspeed reading.

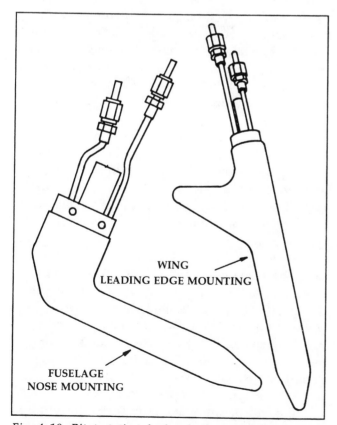

Fig. 4-10. Pitot-static tube heads. (courtesy FAA)

Alternate Air Source

Many unpressurized aircraft use an alternate air source for emergency use, in case of icing, usually vented inside the aircraft. If air pressure is lower inside the aircraft, the altimeter may read higher than normal, the airspeed faster, and the vertical velocity indicator in a climb.

The pressure altimeter (Fig. 4-11) in your aircraft is far from accurate for measuring height, but is safe to use if you understand the way it responds to nonstandard conditions. The pressure altimeter, as explained earlier, is basically a barometer that senses changes in atmospheric pressure that are registered by a gearing mechanism as an altitude indication in feet.

The conversion is based on values called the U.S. Standard Atmosphere, in which sea level temperature and pressure are 15° Centigrade and 29.92 inches of mercury, with a temperature lapse rate of 2° per 1000 feet. An altimeter setting dial provides a means of adjusting the altimeter to non-standard conditions, which can be off as much as 2000 feet between true and indicated altitude. Pilots use the mneumonic phrase: "Flying from high to low, look out below!" to remember which way the altimeter will be off when flying into a low-pressure area. As the air pressure there is lower, the altimeter will read higher than the plane is actually flying.

There are several kinds of altitude you must know about when flying, incidentally:

Indicated altitude is what you read on the altimeter, assuming it is correctly set to show approximate height above mean sea level (MSL).

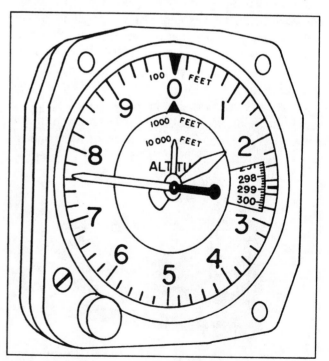

Fig. 4-11. Sensitive altimeter (courtesy FAA)

Pressure altitude is the altitude read on your altimeter when it is adjusted to indicated height above the Standard Datum Plane, a theoretical level where the weight of the atmosphere 29.92″ of mercury.

Density altitude is pressure altitude corrected for nonstandard temperature, a highly important figure to remember in calculating such operations as takeoff from a high airport. Normally you'd use a computer to find the density altitude (DA) by feeding in the actual temperature at the airport runway level. For example: your altimeter is set at 29.92″ and indicates a pressure altitude of 5000 feet, where your Operators Manual tells you you'll need 790 feet for takeoff under standard conditions. But you glance at your outside air temperature (OAT) thermometer and see the actual temperature is 20°C above standard. Your computer now tells you that the DA is above 7000 feet and you'll need closer to 1000 feet for takeoff.

Absolute altitude is the real height above the surface, and can be measured accurately with a radar altimeter.

True altitude is the true height above sea level, a mathematical value determined by computer and therefore based on standard atmospheric conditions (Fig. 4-12).

Radar Altimeters

The radar altimeter provides you with continuous indications of the aircraft's actual height over terrain. The system is a down-looking device that accurately measures the distance between the aircraft and the highest part of terrain you're flying over. The time interval between a transmitted and received radio signal is processed by an airborne computer and converted into an absolute altitude readout. Some radar altimeters have dial presentations and others digital. In the later type, a warning light and audio tone alert the pilot when his aircraft reaches a pre-selected height over the ground.

Rate of climb and rate of descent are important functions of flight. Aside from climbing to altitude fastest, the pilot's main concern normally is in coming down, particularly in IFR flying, when a prepro-

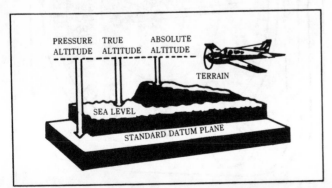

Fig. 4-12. Types of altitude. (courtesy FAA)

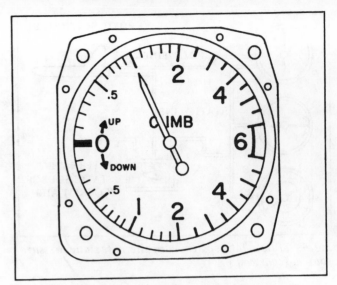

Fig. 4-13. Rate of climb indicator. (courtesy FAA)

grammed rate of descent of say 500 feet per minute must be incorporated in an instrument approach to bring the aircraft to its MDA (Minimum Descent Altitude) at the proper distance from the airport.

To gauge the aircraft's performance in up-and-down flying we use the rate-of-climb indicator (Fig. 4-13), also known as the vertical-speed indicator (VSI). The VSI is contained in an airtight sealed case, connected to the static pressure line through a calibrated leak. Changing pressures contract or expand a diaphragm, connected to the indicating needle through gears and levers.

The VSI automatically compensates for temperature changes. And though it operates from the static pressure source, it is actually a differential pressure instrument, the differential pressure established between the instantaneous static pressure in the diaphragm and the trapped static pressure inside the case.

When the pressures are equalized in level flight, the VSI needle points to zero. But as static pressure in the diaphragm changes during entry to a climb or descent, the needle immediately shows a change of vertical movement, though lag causes a problem in precise readouts. Normally a 6-to-9-second lag is required to either equalize or stabilize the pressures.

Along with the altimeter and turn-and-slip indicator, the airspeed indicator (Fig. 4-14) on your panel provides you with the minimum necessary primary group of instruments called the *partial panel*, or *emergency panel*. No matter how sophisticated your panel layout, the IFR pilot must know how to use these primary instruments for IFR flight, according to Part 91 of the Federal Aviation Regulations.

Your airspeed indicator is designed to measure the difference between ram air pressure from the pitot head and atmospheric pressure from the static source.

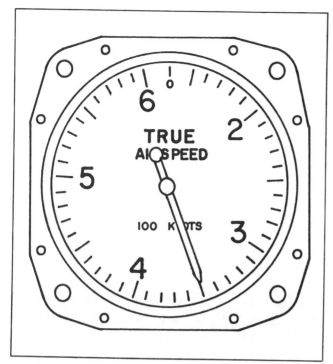

Fig. 4-14. True airspeed indicator. (courtesy FAA)

It is contained within a sealed case containing a diaphragm sensitive to pressure changes. The impact pressure line is connected directly to one side of the diaphragm, while the inside of the case is vented to the static source.

As your aircraft accelerates or decelerates, expansion or contraction of one side of the diaphragm moves the indicator needle across the face by means of gears and levers. The dial may be graduated in terms of *indicated* airspeed, *true* airspeed, *mach* (airspeed converted to a decimal fraction of the speed of sound), or a combination of these values calibrated in miles per hour or in knots.

Several errors can affect your airspeed indicator's readouts. One called *position error* is caused by the static ports sensing erroneous static pressure. *Density error* is introduced by changes in altitude and temperature for which the instrument does not automatically compensate. *Compressibility error* is caused by packing more air into the pitot tube at high velocities, but this error is negligible below about 180 knots and at lower altitudes.

Different Airspeeds

Just as there are several kinds of altitude to worry about, you have several kinds of airspeeds: *indicated airspeed* (IAS) is the value read directly on the face of the instrument. *Calibrated airspeed* (CAS) is the IAS corrected for position and instrument error and is the same as true airspeed (TAS) in standard atmosphere at sea level. *True airspeed* (TAS) is the actual speed at which the aircraft is flying relative to undisturbed air, or the equivalent airspeed corrected for air density

variation from standard sea level values. TAS will increase with altitude while IAS remains the same.

Turning to the engine gauges, we find them normally located to the right side of the panel in single-engine aircraft, away from the standard grouping of flight instruments. For conventional air-cooled aircraft engines, the most important engine gauges are the *tachometer, manifold pressure gauge, cylinder head temperature gauge, exhaust temperature gauge,* and *fuel flow meter,* but not necessarily in that order.

The *tachometer* (Fig. 4-15) is simply a revolution counter that tells you how fast the crankshaft is rotating. With a constant-speed propeller, the tach is adjusted by the propeller pitch control knob, and with a fixed-pitch propeller the throttle is the primary control. With a constant-speed (C/S) propeller, the engine rpm remains constant regardless of power output, which is measured by the *manifold pressure gauge* (MAP), calibrated in inches of mercury (Fig. 4-16). The measurement is taken in the intake manifold and directly indicates the throttle position. At full throttle, full atmospheric pressure is admitted to the engine and the gauge will read normally somewhere between 28 and 29 inches on a standard day at sea level.

On takeoff, the propeller pitch control is positioned for high rpm, and when the throttle is opened, a governor permits the propeller blades to twist to fine pitch to absorb all the available power from the engine.

Climb power is achieved by first reducing the MAP with the throttle, then resetting the tachometer with the pitch control to the proper setting, as prescribed in your Aircraft Operators Manual, perhaps "24-square"—24" MAP and 2400 rpm. Cruise power likewise may be set to whatever value you want, normally about 70-75% of rated horsepower. Lower power settings are used for endurance or long-distance economy flying.

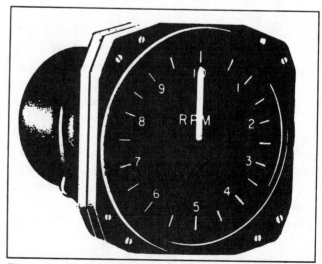

Fig. 4-15. Tachometer. (courtesy FAA)

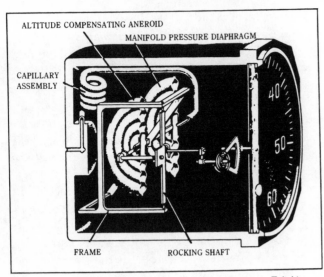

Fig. 4-16. Manifold pressure gauge. (courtesy FAA)

Mixture Control

Once in a cruise mode, the wise pilot will adjust the fuel-air mixture ratio for improved engine efficiency, greater fuel economy, smoother engine operation, longer spark plug life, reduced maintenance cost, and more desirable engine temperatures at cruise altitudes.

Fuel flow, either through a carbureted or fuel-injected induction system, must be manually adjusted in most planes for most efficient fuel/air ratio for efficient combustion within the engine's cylinders. As air density varies with both temperature and altitude, it's important to understand when and how to adjust the mixture control to obtain best performance, fuel economy, and maximum TBO (time between overhaul) engine life.

Generally you should lean out the engine:

☐ Any time the power setting is 75% or less at *any* altitude (full rich mixture is used for climb power through 5000 feet density altitude).

☐ At high-altitude airports lean to taxi, take off, fly the pattern and land.

☐ For landings at airports below 5000 feet DA, adjust the mixture for descent as required to keep the engine running smoothly, going to full rich prior to landing.

The "tach method" is used to lean engines with fixed or variable pitch propellers by many pilots. Establish the desired cruise power setting as indicated in the Operating Manual, then gradually lean the mixture from full rich until the tach reading peaks. For best economy operation, the mixture is first leaned from full rich to max power, then further leaned until a roughness develops. Now enrich the mixture just enough to obtain smooth operation.

The so-called "engine-rough" method of leaning is used with either fixed or variable pitch propellers on engines equipped only with float-type carburetors. With this method, the throttle is set to the proper power setting (75 percent or less), then the engine is leaned until it starts running rough. Now enrichen the mixture slightly until the engine again runs smoothly. It will then be operating near the best economy power setting.

The "fuel-flow meter" method of leaning may be used for either fixed or variable-pitch propeller, and the Operating Manual of aircraft so equipped with fuel-flow gauges will give you the proper fuel-flow settings to use.

EGT Use

Perhaps the most precise leaning procedure is with an EGT (exhaust temperature gauge), for use with any type propeller. Normally, peak EGT occurs at the rich side of the best economy mixture range. Make sure your engine's manufacturer approves peak EGT operation, which not only provides essentially minimum specific fuel consumption, but also some 95 percent of your engine's maximum power capability for a given rpm and MAP. Further, engine operation at peak EGT is smooth.

In flying from high airports such as Denver (5000 feet DA or higher), use lean mixture for taxiing, takeoff, descent and landing:

☐ On start-up and taxi, lean the engine at 1000 rpm until you get a peak rpm, then enrich the mixture slightly.

☐ Prior to takeoff, go to full throttle and lean mixture. (With a fixed-pitch propeller lean to max rpm, then enrich slightly). With a C/S prop on a carbureted engine, lean to engine smoothness, and if an EGT gauge is available, lean to +100 degree on the rich side

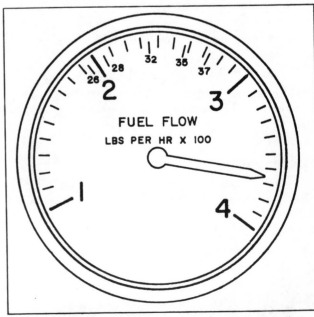

Fig. 4-17. Fuel-flow indicator. (courtesy FAA)

of peak. With a fuel-injected engine, lean to the correct fuel flow setting given in the Operating Manual (Fig. 4-17).

Always lean at traffic pattern altitude before landing at high airports, but only after you have set up maximum power. This ensues max power available in the event of a go-around.

A big part of the total energy consumed by burning fuel is lost as heat within the engine, and more heat is created by moving parts. This heat must be removed for proper control of the fuel-air mixture burning rate, and manufacturers of aircraft engines provides charts of cooling air requirements.

So keep a sharp eye on the three heat gauges available to insure long engine life and most efficient operation—the cylinder head temperature gauge (CHT), the oil temperature gauge, and the exhaust temperature gauge (EGT). Normally, this is done by keeping the needles in the green arc. If you see red, something's amiss!

Chapter 5
Radio
Navigation

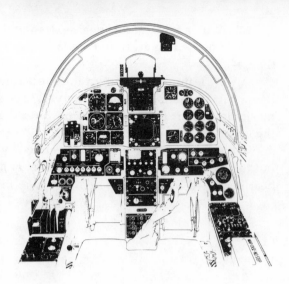

The pilot of an aircraft, like the captain of a ship, holds supreme responsibility for the safe progress of his flight; don't let anybody tell you differently. The cockpit is his command post. The instruments, levers, gauges, and switches are under his direct control with the exception of specific duties delegated to the copilot, or second officer, and the flight engineer.

But there is a difference in command authority today and the way it was before. Now we have our vast Federal Airways System to assist us in flying through controlled airspace, a growing segment of the sky wherein the pilot is required by federal law to coordinate his flight's progress by radio with a vast team of experts. These experts share the pilot's responsibility for decision-making in conducting his flight from takeoff to landing.

Today, navigation and communications are no longer distinctly separate aspects of cross-country flight. They are closely interrelated procedures required during instrument flight in controlled airspace using electronic ground and airborne aids. A basic understanding of their nature and function is required of all pilots using the system.

First, we should remember that the radio frequencies we use in navigation/communication procedures extend over a broad range of frequencies ranging from 20 *kiloHertz* (kHz) to over 30,000 *MegaHertz* (MHz). Because different groups of frequencies within this broad range produce different effects in transmission, we classify them into groups of frequency bands according to their differences:

Band	Frequency	Range
Low Frequency (L/F)	30	to 300 kHz
Medium-Frequency (M/F)	300	to 3000 kHz
High-Frequency (H/F)	3000 kHz	to 30 MHz
Very-High-Frequency (VHF)	30	to 300 MHz
Ultra-High-Frequency (UHF)	300	to 3000 MHz

All matter has a varying degree of conductivity or resistance to radio wave transmission, and the earth itself acts as the greatest resistor to radio waves. Radiated energy that travels close to the ground induces a voltage in the ground that subtracts energy from the wave, decreasing (attenuating) its strength as distance from the transmitting antenna becomes greater.

Trees, buildings, and mineral deposits all affect attenuation to varying degrees. Radiation in the upper atmosphere is likewise affected as its energy is absorbed by molecules of air, moisture, and dust. Characteristics of radio wave propagation vary according to the frequency of the radiated signal, thus determining the design, use, and limitations of both ground and airborne equipment.

LF Radio Waves

Low-frequency radio waves radiate from an antenna in all directions. Part of the energy travels along the ground (*ground wave*) until the energy is dissipated. The rest of the radiated energy travels upward into space (*sky wave*) and would be lost were it not reflected in the ionosphere by highly charged particles (ions) caused by solar radiation. Reflection of radio signals back to earth permits reception of these signals at varying distances from the transmitter, determined by the height and density of the ionosphere and the angle at which the radiated wave strikes the ionosphere. The height and density of the ionosphere are determined by time of day, season, and latitude, since solar radiation is involved.

The distance between the transmitting antenna and the point where the sky wave first returns to the ground is called the *skip distance*. The distance between the point where the ground wave can no longer be received and the sky wave returned is referred to as the *skip zone*. Since solar radiation varies the position and density of the ionosphere, large changes occur in skip distance at dawn and dusk, when signal-fading becomes more prevalent.

With high-frequency wave propagation, attenuation of the ground wave is so large that it is of little use, except at very short distances from the transmitter. Thus the sky wave must be utilized. Since it reflects back and forth between the ionosphere and the ground, it may be utilized over long distances— up to 12,000 miles.

Very-high-frequency transmissions produce practically no ground waves and ordinarily no reflection from the ionosphere. Thus we only use VHF signals when both transmitting and receiving antennas are high enough above the ground to permit a direct wave signal, known as *line-of-sight* transmission. This limitation must be understood when using VHF/UHF equipment in your aircraft. The range of VHF/UHF transmission obviously increases with altitude above the curvature of the earth. To "guesstimate" the VHF/UHF transmission range in nautical miles, simply multiply the square root of your altitude in feet by 1.23. Thus in flying at 3600 feet above flat terrain, multiply $60 \times 1.23 = 73.8$ NM, the maximum distance from the transmitter you can receive the signals.

Low-frequency airborne equipment is highly subject to interference from static, whether caused by lightning discharges or electrostatic discharges from the aircraft surfaces, while signals in higher-frequency bands remain static-free. Precipitation static may be produced when flying through rain or snow, due to charged particles that adhere to the aircraft, create a charge by friction or divide into charged fragments on impact.

Precip Static

At lower altitudes, "precip" static is quite common when you encounter moderate to heavy rain. Sometimes it appears accompanied by St. Elmo's Fire, a corona discharge that lights up the aircraft surfaces where maximum static discharge occurs. I once observed a beautiful, if startling, "pinwheel" effect as St. Elmo's Fire covered the metal propeller of my aircraft, flying through a rain storm near Las Vegas, Nevada. Showers of sparks flew off the blade tips, creating the effect of a miniature galaxy. Radio communication was for a time useless.

Precip static is also common in very high cloud or in dust storms, where high winds pick up and carry aloft substantial amounts of solid particles. It can also result from atmospheric electrical fields in thunderstorm clouds (as I found out!). Ice crystal static may be encountered flying at high altitudes, where cirrus clouds are present, or even in altostratus or nimbocumulus clouds in wintertime.

Another bothersome source of frequency interference are FM radio broadcasts operating in the VHF frequency range—the frequency oscillations in a portable FM radio operated in an aircraft will affect the aircraft's navigation receivers, distorting their readings, so be careful not to listen to ball games on FM radio while navigating by radio!

Radio navigation systems commonly used today combine VOR (*V*ery-High-Frequency *O*mnidirectional *R*ange) with additional electronic aids, plus ground-controlled radar, which have replaced the earlier four-course low-frequency radio ranges where pilots flew along electronic beams, produced by overlapping A (. -) and N (- .) signals.

The NOR omnirange is now the primary navigation facility for civil aviation in our National Airspace System. Being a VHF facility, it eliminates the bothersome atmospheric static and other problems of the low-frequency system it replaced. VOR stations generate directional information, providing 360 magnetic courses TO and FROM the VOR station, called *radials*, which are oriented from the transmitter. Thus, if you're flying southbound on a heading of 180 degrees toward a VOR station, you're following the 360 radial until you cross the station. Then the flag in your VOR instrument switches from TO to FROM and you're flying outbound on the 180-degree radial.

The frequency range of VOR stations extends from 108 to 118 MHz and signals may be received at least 40 miles out from the station at minimal IFR flight altitudes. The station you're tuned into is identified every five seconds by a standard three-letter ID code or a combination of code and voice, the latter reporting every 15 seconds. You can also use the VOR channel for normal voice communication with no interference to its navigational signal.

VOR Receivers

VOR receivers come in a variety of designs and styles, but all have at least five common components:

☐ *Frequency Selector:* a knob or crank manually rotated to select any desired frequency from 108.0 to 118.0 MHz.

☐ *Course Selector:* By turning the OBS (Omni Bearing Selector) the desired course is selected and displayed either in a window or under an index pointer.

☐ *Course Deviation Indicator* (CDI): The deviation indicator consists of a dial over which a hinged needle moves laterally. The needle centers when the aircraft is on the selected radial or its reciprocal. Full needle deflection to either side indicates that you're 10 degrees or more off course. In returning to on-course, always turn the aircraft *toward the needle* (Fig. 5-1).

☐ *To-From Indicator:* This indicator shows whether the selected course will take you TO or FROM

Fig. 5-1. Course Deviation Indicator (CDI).

the station and does *not* tell you which way your aircraft is heading, to or from the station.

□ *Flags:* These or other signal strength indicators tell you whether the signal strength is sufficient for reliable instrument readouts.

There are many excellent VOR flight procedures for orientation or navigation, but such procedures belong rather in a flight manual than a description of cockpit instrumentation, so we'll skip them here.

For the pilot in a hurry, an excellent time-saver for cross-country radio navigation is DME (Distance Measuring Equipment). Used in conjunction with the nationwide VOR system, it gives you immediate readout of your geographic position with a glance at the VOR/DME indicators (Fig. 5-2). This is a modern version of the old DR (Dead Reckoning) procedure of plotting position by time/distance yardsticks, by triangulation using a single or dual VOR, or a VOR and L/F receiver. Instead, VOR/DME gives you distance and bearing to or from your station right now.

In operation, the DME unit transmits an interrogating signal, consisting of a pair of HF pulses, which is received by the DME transponder antenna at the ground station. This triggers a second pair of pulses that come back to the aircraft's DME, which measures the elapsed time between the second interrogating and reply pulses and converts this time measurement into a mileage reading on the instrument panel, called the *slant-range distance*. Should the aircraft be directly above the ground station, the DME receiver thus would display altitude in nautical miles above the transmitter. Slant-range error is negligible

if the aircraft is one mile or more from the ground facility for each 1000 feet of altitude above the facility's elevation.

ADF Receivers

The most versatile low-frequency radio navigation aid available to the general aviation pilot is the automatic direction finder, or ADF (Fig. 5-3), a homing and direction-finding receiver that utilizes transmissions from commercial broadcast stations, radio range stations, or nondirectional radio beacons (NDBs).

World War II pilots gave them the name "bird dogs" because they always point directly to the station. All you have to do is follow the pointer to arrive over it. In countries such as Canada and Mexico, where VOR routes may be scarce in the vicinity of your flight, the ADF is indispensable for radio navigation.

There's one problem common to all ADF receivers using loop antennae, called *ambiguity*. In use, the loop is rotated until its plane lies at right angles to the signal source, when a minimum signal strength or null is reached, but the problem is whether the station is in "front" or "behind" the loop. To solve the ambiguity problem, a "sense" antenna is coupled to the loop so that the ADF indicator needle always points toward the transmitting station.

By setting the full circle dial, marked off in degrees like a compass card, with zero at the top, the

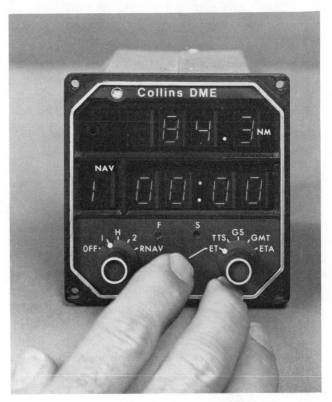

Fig. 5-2. Collins Micro Line Digital DME Indicator.

Fig. 5-3. Collins DF-203 automatic direction finding system.

needle points to the relative bearing of the transmitting station. Thus, if you're flying a magnetic course of 300 degrees and the ADF needle points to 45 degrees, the station is 45 degrees to your right, on a bearing of 345 degrees.

Flying by ADF navigation, you can listen to the news or ball games when homing in on a commercial station near an airport, or you can use it for an Instrument Landing System (ILS) approach, using the locator as a primary approach aid.

ILS Approaches

On shooting an ILS approach, authorized ceiling and visibility minimums depend on the kind of ground and airborne equipment being utilized. A typical lightplane VOR receiver may be used as a localizer receiver, with common tuning and indicating equipment, the CDI (Course Deviation Indicator) indicating "on course" on final approach, just as it does when flying a VOR radial.

A big help shooting a VOR approach is a *localizer glideslope indicator*, sometimes called a *cross-pointer indicator*. The crossed horizontal (glideslope) and vertical (localizer) needles move freely through standard five-dot deflections to indicate position on the localizer course and glide path.

The localizer needle indicates, by deflection, the color sector in which the aircraft is flying, regardless of the position or heading of the aircraft. Rotation of the omni bearing selector has no effect on operation of the localizer needle. Some indicators show blue and yellow sectors to the left and right of the centerline position of the needle; on instruments with no color shown, the needle deflects left in the blue sector, right in the yellow sector.

Thus, when flying inbound on the front course (Fig. 5-4) or outbound on the back course, the needle is deflected toward the on-course and you turn toward the needle to correct your track. Conversely, when inbound on the back course or outbound on the front course, you turn away from the direction of the needle's deflection to get back on the centerline (Fig. 5-5).

With an ADF tuned to the outer compass locator, orientation on the localizer course is simplified. The localizer course is quite narrow, resulting in high needle sensitivity, which permits accurate centerline orientation on final approach to the runway. Incidentally, such high sensitivity tends to encourage over-controlling, until you develop a smooth flying technique in making small course corrections. Some pilots like to skid the aircraft rather than banking it in making small corrections.

Glideslope needle deflections warn that you are above or below the glideslope. When above it, the needle is deflected downward and vice versa. The trick is to establish a proper rate of descent on glideslope interception, then use very small corrections to hold to it (Fig. 5-6).

Marker beacon receivers operate on a frequency of 75 MHz and may provide both aural and visual indication of passage over a VHF marker beacon. A

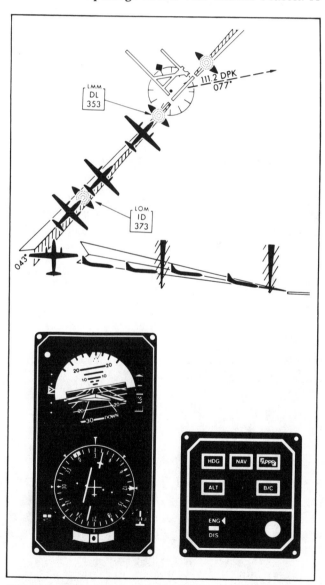

Fig. 5-4. Shooting front-course approach with Collins Low-Profile Flight Control System.

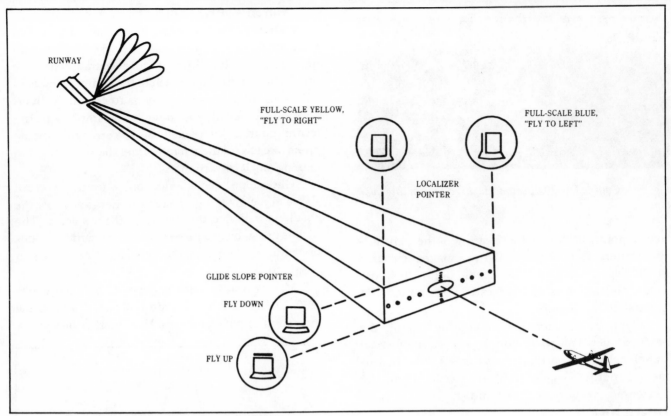

Fig. 5-5. Glideslope information. (courtesy FAA)

white light is actuated over the "Z" or fan marker; blue and yellow lights indicate passage over the outer and inner markers on an ILS approach (Fig. 5-7).

Although no communications equipment is required when you fly in uncontrolled airspace, Federal Aviation Regulations, when you fly IFR in controlled airspace, demand that you be equipped with two-way communication capability appropriate to the ground stations being used, maintain a continuous listening watch on the appropriate frequency, and report by radio as required.

1½ Radios

A useful installation is called the "one and one-half" system. It incorporates both communications and navigation radios in a single, compact unit, rather than requiring the pilot to search all over his panel to

Fig. 5-6. Shooting ILS approach at Santa Monica Airport.

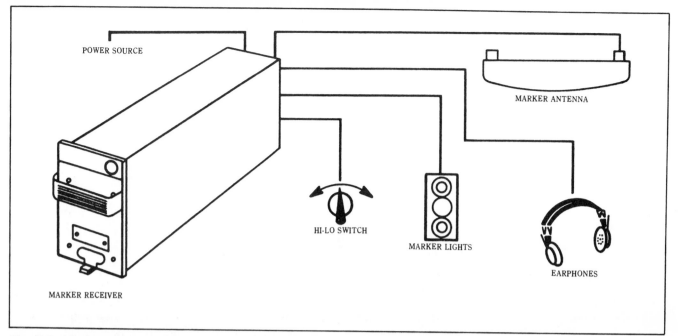

POWER SOURCE

MARKER ANTENNA

HI-LO SWITCH

MARKER LIGHTS

EARPHONES

MARKER RECEIVER

Fig. 5-7. Marker receiver system diagram. (courtesy FAA)

locate switches, selectors, and associated indicators to tune and operate his radios. The "One and One-Half" enables you to communicate with the required ground facilities on the transceiver (a combined transmitter/receiver while tuned on the separate "One-Half" part of the set to a VOR station.

Operation of the COMM side is simple. A volume switch serves as the ON/OFF switch for both COMM and NAV sides, while a squelch knob can be rotated to cut down background noise. If you're tuning in a weak signal, decrease the squelch, otherwise once you've set the control at a comfortable level, leave it alone, except to check on receiver sensitivity.

This system may be expanded with installation of additional radios and centralized control units for fast selection of receivers and transmitters, added in a "building block" concept. These extra radios may be extremely helpful when flying into IFR weather, in supplying you with frequent changes of COMM channels already set up.

Modern VHF COMM transceivers like the Collins VHF-250 offer up to 720 25-kHz-spaced channels to meet the present and future needs of the FAA's air traffic control system, all frequencies generated by a single-crystal frequency synthesizer for high accuracy, small size, and reliability.

Chapter 6
Is Man Obsolete?

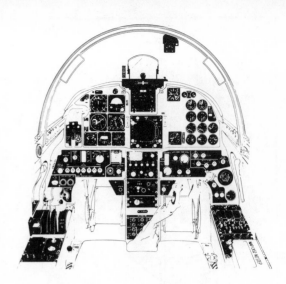

The lonely world of the fighter pilot went through a dramatic change in the 1950s, when for the first time the United States Air Force, Navy, and Marine Corps were at last equipped with jet fighter planes. All other combat types immediately became anachronistic in modern warfare as combat crewmen found themselves encapsulated in pressurized cockpits linked to life-support equipment with umbilicals, much like an astronaut, and completely dependent on instrumentation to serve as extensions of their senses.

Jet pilots flying combat patrol missions over Korea became a new breed of aerial gladiator with responsibilities undreamed of just a decade earlier, during World War II.

The problems of flying a simple fighter mission in that war were well described by J. H. (Dutch) Kindelberger, board chairman of North American Aviation, makers of the swept-wing F-86 Sabre jet fighter. The Sabre first flew October 1, 1947, at Muroc, California (now Edwards Air Force Base) as the XP-86 with a 4000-pound thrust Chevrolet-built J35-C-3 jet engine, and went into production as the F-86A with an engine of 5200 pounds thrust. On September 1, 1948 the third F-86A-1 built set a world speed record of 670.98 mph.

Sabre Jets Go to War

Production of 554 F-86As ended in December, 1950, when the first Sabre wing arrived in Korea. On December 17, Sabres flew their first mission and scored their first kill. By July 1953 they had flown 87,177 sorties and scored 814 enemy kills with 224 Sabre losses. Kindelberger touched the heart of Sabre jet flying in pointing out that "At an altitude of about eight miles above the Earth, the pilot and his airplane are in a very thin and very cold atmosphere, where the temperature is about 60 below zero and the pressure about 2 pounds per square inch, as compared with almost 15 pounds per square inch at sea level.

"Breathing free in this atmosphere, the pilot could not remain conscious more than about 30 seconds and could not survive for more than a few minutes. He must be enclosed in a heated and pressurized compartment, and he must have pure oxygen pushed into his lungs under pressure. The thin air also handicaps the engine, to the extent that its effective thrust is barely enough to win the fight against the weight and drag of the airplane. Therefore the pilot must make every maneuver with delicate precision."

Considering the fate of the pilot of the then-new jet fighter aircraft, Kindelberger observed that "He finds himself packed into the sleek fuselage of a jet fighter with about one hundred controls to operate and twenty-four instruments to observe, plus a dozen indicator or warning lights to keep an eye on. In the fuselage with him is electrical and electronic gear equal in complexity to the combined circuits of a city power system, a radio broadcasting station, a TV broadcasting station, and the fire control system of a battleship. Under him and around him and behind him run hydraulic lines, fuel lines, heating and cooling ducts, and oxygen lines. A few feet away is a giant blowtorch delivering as much effective power as three large diesel locomotives. And there he sits, loaded down with protective clothing, parachute, G-suit, crash helmet, oxygen mask, and an acute bellyache caused by expansion of his body gas at high altitude.

"Now, the reason he is eight miles above the Korean landscape is to find another airplane and if possible to shoot it down. Here his senses prove pretty inadequate, for the reasons that both his airplane and the enemy airplane are moving fast, and that his spatial perception is impaired by such things as lack of reference points, most of the clouds being far below and even the horizon being just an indistinct haze far in the distance. Also, the sky above is a very dark blue in which it is almost impossible to see anything unless he catches a glint of sun on metal. Not only are his senses inadequate to see the other plane and judge its relative position and speed, but his reaction time is often too slow for proper control of his airplane and his guns.

"In all this there is a pretty strong psychological factor, also. Remember that the pilot is a very intricate machine moving fast through an environment in which he cannot exist without the aid of his equipment. In the back of his mind is the emergency in which he may have to leave the aircraft by actuating the controls which blow off the canopy and fire his ejection seat away from the airplane, after which comes the prospect of a perilous and very cold descent to enemy territory."

Who Needs Pilots?

Kindelberger pointed out that "From this brief description of some phases of a present-day fighter mission we see that our flying machines are rapidly approaching capabilities that are penalized rather than aided by the presence of a human pilot. We have to give the man something to breathe and create an artificial atmospheric pressure for him. We have to cool and warm his body as the ambient temperature varies. We have to provide for his physical volume and weight and comfort, and we have to put in scores of devices to insure his survival in an emergency.

"Finally, because his senses are not sufficiently acute and his reaction time is not fast enough to enable him to guide the machine in all the split-second phases of its military mission, we must install devices that not only control the machine automatically, but also waste extra weight and space informing the human pilot what the machine has been told.

"A good example of this," said Kindelberger, "is the system of flight controls. Because of the tremendous loads encountered and the physical limitation of the pilot, we have gone into what we call an *irreversible power control system*, wherein none of the air load is transferred back to the pilot's stick. However, since the pilot has been taught to fly by feel, we have to give him a wholly artificial load on the control stick, in exactly the right amount for all maneuvers under infinitely varying conditions. To work out this problem, we have developed a system or science called 'synthesis of reactions,' which duplicates in the laboratory all the mechanical, hydraulic, electronic and human linkages involved. Now this synthesis of reactions utilizes just about every known field of physical science and a few that haven't been invented yet. It is just one example of the technical Hell we are going through because the machine is getting so far ahead of the man."

Flying Tornados

To keep up with the fast pace of technical progress in military aircraft, a new device has been developed to permit the pilot of a supersonic jet to make a bombing run at 200 feet altitude flying 700 mph without glancing down at his instrument panel. It is known as the HUD (Head-Up Display), and its use is well described by British Aerospace's Chief Pilot David Eagles, in a report on such a mission in the new swing-wing, all-weather Tornado (Fig. 6-1) now being flown by the armed forces of Britain, Germany, and Italy.*

"As you walk around the aircraft," says Eagles, "you'll be surprised at its small size, an aid to survival in the low-level attack game. Its empty weight is around 30,000 pounds, but it is densely packed and has about the same surface area as the F-18."

The large, ungainly nose of the Tornado provides room for a wide, roomy cockpit. "After the cockpits of the BAC Lightning and British/French Jaguar," says Eagles, "this one looks like a ballroom!" The size of the nose radome itself was dictated by the dimensions and layout of the two antennas for the ground-mapper and the terrain-following radars, the first of which the navigator checks with built-in test equipment. The cockpit layout is fairly conventional in the Tornado, and is dominated by the big, five-inch lens Head-Up Display and the Head-Down Repeater projected map display in the center.

An "E" scope high up on the left front panel (Fig. 6-2). gives raw returns from the terrain-following radar, and the hand controller—a small handle just behind the throttles with various switches—enables the pilot to control some of the HUD attack symbology and provides inputs to the aircraft's main computer.

The rear cockpit (Fig. 6-3) represents a much greater change from convention, says Eagles. The same roomy cockpit space has allowed a logical panel layout, but the front panel at eye level is all electronic with a combined radar and projected map display flanked by two TV tabular displays and associated keyboards. The radar hand controller sits on a pedestal between the operator's knees and the TV. Tabs allow dialogue with the computer, which stores 65,000 bits of information in its memory.

Two seats provide greater opportunity for mission success than a single-seater, says Eagles. "It is easy," he explains, "to fly a single-seat auto terrain-following bombing attack through weather to take out a planned target, but if another type of target is spot-

---

Reprinted by permission from Air Force Magazine, June 1980. Copyright 1980, Air Force Association.

Fig. 6-1. Takeoff of Tornado 03 carrying eight 1000-lb. bombs, two large external fuel tanks and two ECM pods. (courtesy British Aerospace)

ted on the way, if a change of target is ordered en-route, if an evading diversion from planned track is made necessary, preventing planned navigation up-dating, if a single failure occurs necessitating manual instead of auto terrain folowing—in any case of these not unusual cases you would be glad to have someone to share the extra workload while you keep the aircraft out of the weeds."

On the Deck

Down on the deck, says Eagles, "The smoothness of the ride here isn't just an added tourist attraction. It makes it possible to monitor the terrain-following, track-keeping, and the HUD attack symbology with-out distraction or fatigue in all-weather attack condi-tions."

Eagles now describes an actual Tornado terrain-following bombing mission: "Approaching the bombing range, let's set up for a single pass laydown attack, dropping our eight 1000-pound bombs in a stick. With terrain-following selected and hard ride, we can be sure that we are following the ground contours as closely as any aircraft at 600 knots can do.

"Wind down the 'clearance height' setting knob to the minimum level and you are down in the weeds, giving the hardest possible task to any defending weapon system. It's comforting to know that there is triplex attitude-monitoring in the automatic terrain-following system and that you'll get an automatic pull-up before the aircraft is handed back to you in the event of a failure. The only trips to date with the system have been caused by discrepancies in sensitiv-ity between the different attitude sensors, finally

ironed out after many hours of terrain-following over the Black Forest in southern Germany.

"At about twenty miles to target, the navigator selects the weapon package, the 'attack' mode on the

Fig. 6-2. Front cockpit of Panavia Tornado. (courtesy British Aerospace)

Fig. 6-3. Rear cockpit of Panavia Tornado, trainer version. (courtesy British Aerospace)

TV display and the 'stabilized' mode on the combined map and radar display. The stabilized mode brings the computed target or radar offset to screen center, overlaid with an aiming marker. An automatic radar identification tilt facility along with the stabilized mode makes the task of target identification and possible target marker position refinement a low-workload task.

"In the front seat, you will be checking the attack progress through the HUD with hand on stick ready to take over from the autopilot if you should be able to identify the target visually and see an aiming error.

"As the navigator refines the target position using his own hand controller, you will notice the HUD aiming marker move to superimpose on the new target ground position and also feel the aircraft react to the autopilot adjusting the aircraft track to achieve the correct release solution. The throttles can be left alone since IAS (Indicated Air Speed) is being controlled by the auto throttle.

"A circle around the aircraft symbol in the HUD unwinds to show the number of seconds to automatic bomb release. Some time before the pilot would see the target in visual conditions, the navigator will have finished aiming and the laser range-finder will be ranging on the target position to give the weapon system very accurate plan range and aircraft height

information. You will squeeze the stick-mounted pickle button, which is the pilot's 'commit' signal. You can prevent release at any time up to the last second by releasing the button.

Along for the Ride

"If the European weather maintains its usual form, your only contribution to the bomb drop as pilot will be to monitor the whole exercise to ensure safety. There is absolutely nothing to be gained by switching to a 'Phase 2' attack—bringing the pilot into the loop. But if the target is seen anywhere but under the marker, or if a more attractive alternate target is seen, you can use the 'eyeball' on the hand controller to move the marker accurately over the new target and let the autopilot take care of the track change required, or you can take over control of the aircraft to hand-fly it to a release point. In this case, you'll be glad that Tornado's handling qualities are so consistently excellent, because dragging an aircraft out of autopilot to pull a hard turn at 200 feet and 600 knots with only two or three seconds to go to release demands nothing less.

"The stick of eight 1000-pound bombs rippling off the belly comes through as a slight shuddering and results in a noticeable acceleration, having ditched the drag. The plan would now be to stay fast and low, back to where it's friendly."

And how does Tornado handle on a high and hot mission involving an air strike from the region of the tropopause? Says Eagles: "With four semisubmerged Skyflash air-to-air missiles and two Sidewinders, Tornado will cruise out at medium altitude and remain on combat air patrol with the wing swept forward. Its radar incorporates a multitarget track-while-scan facility and gives excellent look-down performance. After high-level target contract, the air defense Tornado will accelerate to a high supersonic speed, giving a capability to take out targets to altitudes well in excess of 55,000 feet, by using a combination of aircraft zoom and missile performance. Interception can be carried out 'hands off' and in all weather, right down to the trees.

"When approaching Mach 0.8 at 25,000 feet, the wing is brought back to the mid 45-degree position, giving reduced drag in maneuvering. Leading edge slat is still available at 45 degrees but the maneuver flap is inhibited. Carefree maneuvering up to high incidence is provided courtesy of the spin prevention and incidence limiting system. The system allows the pilot to get the maximum performance out of the aircraft with total confidence—a requirement that is here to stay in modern combat aircraft.

"Slamming to combat power at 25,000 feet starts a healthy airspeed increase and the wing is swept right back at about Mach 0.92. The 45-degree wing is, of course, good for high supersonic speeds, but we are after optimum acceleration. There is slight Mach 'noise' at Mach 0.98, but all is smooth and quiet at the jump-up to supersonic speed and the optimum acceleration is achieved by building up to around 550 knots IAS and then maintaining that in a climb to the tropopause.

Going Home

"At the tropopause our rate of Mach progress depends, of course, on the OAT (outside air temperature) and the aircraft's handling qualities remain good. Let's cut the afterburner now and drop the nose to pick up 800 knots IAS on the way home. Even at this speed the turbulence encountered on plunging through cumulus clouds comes through as very soft-edged aircraft reaction.

"Airbrakes can be selected at any time, but we don't need airbrakes to decelerate from 800 knots. Idle power has the desired effect initially, and below

about 600 knots the wing can be swept forward to 45 degrees, which also helps.

"Back at home base, the weather is 200 feet and a mile in rain and we position for an ILS approach. Mid flaps and gear are dropped at 300 knots and 250 knots respectively. The pattern is flown at 200 knots with 'auto approach' selected and speed is bled off to 140 knots for final approach after full flaps have been lowered.

"At 200 feet the runway lights appear out of the murk, and the autopilot is disconnected by the thumb switch on the stick. Roundout, and as the main wheels touch down, the lift dumpers extend and kill any tendency to float. At the same time the reverser buckets snap out at about 85 percent rpm, and as the nosewheel touches, both engines are slammed to max power and the brakes are stamped on. The result is the nearest thing to a carrier deck landing that an Air Force pilot is likely to experience. In no wind, you can come to a full stop with ease in less than 1500 feet!"

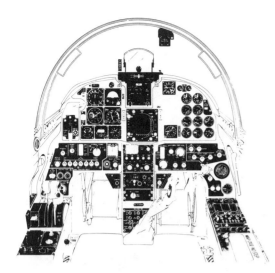

Chapter 7

Do-It-Yourself Cockpits

Airmen who build their own aircraft have the advantage of choosing an instrument panel design and layout most suitable to their needs. An aerobatic pilot would want different kinds of instruments from those favored by one whose primary interest is cross-country flying, where navigation instruments are important. A pilot who regularly flies on instruments would require a more sophisticated panel than the weekend VFR flyer, who seldom strays far from his airport. Yet all pilots favor the simplest, most efficient panel design that properly groups the control, performance, and NAV/COM instruments.

For sheer simplicity, glance into the cockpit of most any powered ultralight flying machine. Instrumentation will range anywhere from zero to maybe two or three gauges, whatever the builder can afford. Typically, Ken Striplin's little F.L.A.C. (Foot Launched Air Cycle) has a single CHT (Cylinder Head Temperature) gauge mounted at cockpit left, to make sure the McCulloch 101 chain saw engine doesn't overheat.

Wade Sellards, of Trona, California, loves to fly over the scorching desert country looking for mine sites and archeological diggings from his midwing Stits Flut-R-Bug monoplane, and in that kind of piloting you don't even need a radio. Atop his panel is the ubiquitous magnetic compass, and below it are only two flight instruments—a sensitive altimeter and an airspeed indicator that goes clear up to 200 mph! As Wade takes off, flies, and lands at 53 mph, who needs a Machmeter? His panel also is replete with a carburetor heat push-pull control, a mag switch, a tachometer, an oil pressure gauge and a water temperature gauge. For an air-cooled A-65 Continental? Well, he couldn't afford an oil temperature gauge, so he simply adapted a water temperature dial to operate off a sensor in the oil sump.

Homebuilt F-104

At the other end of the complexity scale was the "homebuilt" Lockheed F-104 Starfighter (Fig. 7-1) which Darryl Greenamyer assembled from junkyard bits and pieces scrounged virtually from all over the world. Greenamyer, a well-known race pilot, named his little jet bomb the *Red Baron* and outfitted the instrument panel with a bunch of super-sophisticated dials and radios (Fig. 7-2).

At top center, where he couldn't miss it, he installed a huge, ball-shaped military attitude indicator of the non-tumbling variety that works upside down or rightside up. To the right he installed a Machmeter to tell him when he was flying faster than sound, or close to it, and down below he put in a G-meter to measure acceleration forces. Fuel-flow meters, jet nozzle position indicator, H_2O (water) flow meter for the injection system, and other such stuff were scattered across the panel, with the radio and navigational avionics mounted below.

In between these extremes, you'll find a wide variety of cockpit arrangements planned to suit the individual desires of the homebuilders. By and large, most builders group their flight instruments where they are most visible—to the left in a side-by-side aircraft, with engine instruments at right.

A Special T-18

Darrel Hirsch, a Northrop engineer who built his own Thorp T-18 (Fig. 7-3) in his garage in Malibu, California, took special care in laying out his instrument panel (Fig. 7-4), with the flight instruments grouped around his gyro attitude indicator as his primary instrument. Under it he installed a Piper Aircraft directional gyro (DG). Used together, these two instruments help him maintain a desired heading by checking the DG reading against the attitude indi-

Fig. 7-1. Darryl Greenamyer's F-104.

cator to make sure the wings are level and the aircraft is not turning.

To establish a rate turn, Hirsch establishes the correct bank for his particular cruise speed by cross-checking the attitude indicator with a glance to lower left at a two-minute turn-and-slip indicator.

For precise airspeed control, he looks left from the attitude indicator to the airspeed indicator, cross-checking the aircraft nose attitude to the rate-of-climb indicator, to the right of the DG.

Because airspeed is controlled by pitch attitude and climb or descent by power setting, the tachometer is conveniently installed in Hirsch's T-18 to the right of the sensitive altimeter, which itself is placed to the right of the primary attitude indicator. Actually, as pilots know, pitch and power are used together to maintain the proper vertical airspeed—up, level, or down.

Basically, Hirsch's panel follows the time-tested military arrangement known as the T-panel, you can most quickly shift your eyes left and right, and up and down, from your primary instrument, particularly in weather flying, to reduce strain. Incidentally, the attitude indicator is not necessarily your "primary" instrument—in a climb, your ROC (rate of climb) indicator may be considered primary, with airspeed and power instrument supportive, and in following a magnetic heading, your compass, either magnetic or DG or whatever, may be of primary interest.

Hirsch installed two VOR NAV/COM radios under the flight instruments further to simplify the task of cross-country navigation by radio. Engine gauges are typically at the right—tachometer, cylinder head temperature, exhaust temperature, and a combination oil temperature and oil/fuel pressure gauge all in one hole. At lower right he stuck in a G-meter, handy in case he gets the urge to fly aerobatic maneuvers without overstressing his aircraft, or to monitor severity of turbulence in weather flying.

Fig. 7-2. Greenamyer F-104 cockpit.

With the flexibility offered by designing and building your own airplane, you can plan your instrument panel in almost any way you wish, but it's well to keep in mind the demand for division of attention among many instruments, particularly during IFR flying. A proper division of attention and proper sequence for cross-checking your instruments varies considerably among pilots.

Cross-check technique is a skill acquired to fully grasp what the gauges are telling you without referring to the natural horizon outside the aircraft windscreen. It is influenced by the characteristic manner in which the instruments respond to changes in aircraft attitude and/or power setting.

Instrument Grouping

Flight instruments fall into three groups, by usage—control instruments, performance instruments, and navigation instruments. Control instruments are the attitude and power indicators, and by using them properly you obtain performance required for maintaining level flight, turn, climb or descent, speed, and even takeoff and landing.

While control instruments provide direct and immediate indications of attitude and/or power changes, the responsive indications of performance instruments lag a little—the airspeed indicator, compass, altimeter, turn-and-slip indicator, and VSI (vertical speed indicator).

This lag may be caused either by aircraft inertia or by imperfections in the performance of the instruments themselves, and must be accepted and compensated for in precision instrument flying. However, lag in performance instruments need not interfere with your ability to maintain or smoothly change the attitude and/or power indications. When these are kept under control, the lag factor is negligible and the readouts on your performance indicators will smoothly stabilize or change as expected.

Wise IFR pilots never make flight control movements in response to the lag of performance instruments without first cross-checking their control instruments to insure that they are properly set. The result would be highly erratic flying, as in "chasing

Fig. 7-3. Darrel Hirsch's T-18.

Fig. 7-4. Hirsch's T-18 panel.

the compass" when attempting to catch up with the reading of the magnetic compass indication in a turn. Just remember that the sooner you do apply a correction for a deviation, the smaller the required corrective adjustment of the control instrument will be.

Your attitude indicator is the only instrument you might want to stare at for any length of time—it may take you up to ten seconds properly to enter a turn, during which time you can maintain good attitude control solely by reference to the attitude control indicator as your "primary" instrument.

How to Cross-Check

Good cross-checking technique involves a systematic method of shifting your eyes from your primary instrument to support instruments, as from the attitude indicator to the VSI in a climb mode. Pilots should guard against fixation—staring at the VSI, for example, while neglecting to cross-check the DG to make sure you are maintaining your proper heading.

Power control is far simpler—most pilots know through experience precisely what rpm and manifold pressure to use for a desired flight mode say a 500 rpm rate of climb at a certain airspeed. Pitch and power may become your primary instruments in setting up a climb or descent to achieve the desired airspeed and ROC, cross-checking against the DG to insure you are on course. On an instrument approach, the cross needles of your glideslope indicator may for the moment become primary, to hold a precise left-right course and up-and-down vertical speed, cross-checking against the VSI. These matters, however, properly belong on a manual on how-to-fly and are secondary to the homebuilder's main concern—properly laying out his instrument panel to suit his personal preferences (and pocketbook!).

In addition to the panel instruments mentioned

above, care must be given to positioning of such matters as placement of the engine throttle, mixture control, and propeller pitch control. In single-place or tandem-seating aircraft, the usual position of the "throttle quadrant" is at the left, so that the right hand is free to control the joystick or wheel, in maintaining pitch and roll stability with elevator and ailerons. The rudder pedals, of course, are where you can stomp on them, with either toe brakes or heel brakes. The former are preferred by most builders.

In side-by-side seating arrangements you may want to put the "power console" in center so both pilot and copilot can easily reach the throttle, pitch, and mixture controls. Similarly, a manual flap handle in this arrangement usually is placed between the two pilot seats, to be operated by the right hand of the pilot and left hand of the copilot. Other items such as the magneto and starter switches and circuit breakers can be stuck under the instrument panel, at the left or right side of the cockpit as desired. An all-important, inexpensive and lightweight item you should not overlook is called an OAT—Outside Air Temperature gauge—and can be useful in many ways, other than determining where the freezing level is on a climb through weather. Any deviation from standard atmospheric conditions may be run through a circular computer in a moment to give you a true airspeed or pressure altitude readout.

Minimum Equipment

Although many homebuilders enjoy loading their cockpits up with all the latest, new-fangled gadgetry, others get along well with minimum equipment. A master of this is Don Taylor, a retired USAF Colonel. He built his own lovely little Thorp T-18 and flew it around the world solo with the same kind of navigation stuff other pilots use to fly 50 or a hundred miles (Fig. 7-5).

Instead of investing in expensive VLF, Omega, LORAN, Consolan or other long-range avionics, Taylor simply used a Bendix digital ADF and a single Narco Mark-12 VOR receiver. In flying the Pacific over distances up to 1200 miles non-stop, he simply used old-fashioned dead reckoning to fly in the general direction of his destination, then switched to ADF when he could pick up a commercial broadcasting station or radio beacon. For the last miles he switched to the Mark-12 and homed in on his VOR needle.

It all boils down to good piloting techniques, no matter how much you spend on fancy do-dads in your cockpit, though things like DGs and artificial horizons are nice. I enjoy my ADF radio, if for no other reason than to check en route weather conditions, or listen to a spot of music or news, on a long flight.

On the following pages you will find a wide assortment of cockpit designs and instrument panel layouts reflecting the individual tastes of a number of homebuilders, each one reflecting a personal choice based on pride, efficiency, pilot skill, or pocketbook. This is the first time such a collection of homebuilt aircraft panels has been gathered in one volume, so enjoy!

Fig. 7-5. Don Taylor's T-18 cockpit.

American Eaglet.

American Eaglet panel.

American Eaglet

The American Eaglet self-launching sailplane was designed to provide the soaring enthusiast with good performance at an affordable price. No towplanes are required to launch the Eaglet nor are ground crews required to retrieve it. With an empty weight of 160 pounds, it can easily carry a 12-hp McCulloch MC101B go-kart engine for takeoff and climb to thermal country. The propeller blades fold into the tail to reduce drag when soaring.

A roomy cockpit can handle a 6-foot-2-inch pilot in a reclining position. The instrument panel includes a magnetic compass, variometer, airspeed indicator, and altimeter. The Eaglet has a max L/D of 27:1 @ 45kts; minimum sink of 2.5 fps @ 35kts; V_{max} (smooth air) of 100kts; maneuvering speed of 68kts, and stall at 34kts. It can be built for under $2000 in three to four months of weekend and evening work. Contact: American Eagle, 841 Winslow Court, Muskegon, MI 49441.

Acrojet Special Minijet team.

Acrojet Special Minijet

The world's only two Acrojet Specials flying today are piloted by Bob Bishop and Corky Fornoff of Acrojet Performance, Inc. Both are regular performers at air shows in their "world's smallest" minijets, powered with TRS-18 046 turbojets only 12 inches in diameter and 23 inches long. Engines weigh 78 pounds and develop 202 pounds static thrust.

Numerous internal changes have been made from the Bede BD-5J jet sport plane. Bishop's Acrojet is 80 pounds lighter and uses wing fuel tanks only,

eliminating much plumbing. Steel torque tubes are used instead of aluminum for aileron control, for less springback and faster roll rate. Both Bishop and Fornoff built their own Acrojets.

Flight instruments include a sensitive altimeter, artificial horizon (non-tumbling), and airspeed indicator at top, with Collins Micro Line communications equipment, by which the pilots narrate their airshow routines directly from their cockpits. Turn and slip indicator and VSI are at right, and circuit breakers are installed across the panel's top.

Instrument panel of Acrojet Special.

Bede BD-4.

Bede BD-4

James R. Bede formed Bede Aircraft Inc. to develop plans and kits for his BD-4 design, which can be built either as a two or four-seater. By 1976 more than 2000 sets of plans had been sold and more than 730 aircraft had flown. The majority have tricycle landing gear, fixed, but a few were built with tailwheel-type gear.

Fiberglass wing panel ribs slide over an extruded aluminum spar, which fits over the center section tube. The fuselage is all metal, with aluminum or fiberglass skin. The empennage also is all metal. The two-seater BD-4 uses a 108-hp 0-235-C1 flat four Lycoming; the four-seater version, a Lycoming 0-320 (150 hp) or a Lycoming 0-360 (200 hp) engine.

Wingspan is 25 feet 7 inches; empty weight is 1125 pounds. The BD-4 cruises at 145 mph (two-seater version, 75 percent power). V_{max} for the 200-hp version is 203 mph. A vertical instrument panel carries flight instruments at left and has a slanted sub-panel, which includes engine instruments and electrical switches. Controls include dual yokes with throttle at center.

Bede BD-4 instrument panel.

Bede BD-5 Micro.

Bede BD-5 Micro

Several versions of the Bede BD-5 have appeared since construction of the prototype was begun in 1967. The original version, the BD-5A, used a 40-hp Kiekhaefer engine and had a "butterfly" tail assembly. The BD-5D was a factory-built version of the same model, and the BD-5S was a sailplane version with longer wings.

The popular BD-5G used a new wing section and is fully aerobatic. A jet-powered version, the BD-5J, was powered with a Microturbo TRS-18 turbojet of 202 lb. static thrust, which gave it a speed of 276 mph.

The BD-5 pilot sits in a semi-reclining position in a small cockpit with good visibility. The BD-5G model uses three EGTs (exhaust gas temperature gauges) to monitor the functioning of the three-cylinder Xenoah two-stroke powerplant of 70 hp.

Flight instruments are at the panel's top; engine gauges are below and at right; and switches on a side panel are at right, ahead of a side-mounted wrist control stick.

Bede BD-5 Micro cockpit.

Bitty Bipe, designed by Dick Bailey.

Cockpit of Bitty Bipe.

Bitty Bipe

Bitty Bipe is a tiny little biplane that weighs only 550 pounds empty, is powered with a gutty little 125-hp Lycoming 0-290, has a power loading of only 6.8 pounds per horsepower at max gross weight. It is built to withstand 9 Gs, plus or minus, for unlimited aerobatic flying. The builder, Dick Bailey, is a crop duster.

Roughly 75 percent lighter than a Smith Mini-plane and with 20 percent more power, it can handle such graceful maneuvers as an eight-point slow roll with ease, though it has no inverted fuel system. It loops at 140 mph, rolls at 120, and enters a split-S at 80.

Bitty Bipe has recently been owned by Doctor Arthur M. Compher, an FAA Medical Examiner, who shared his single seat with two pilot friends, Doug Johnson, a flight instructor, and Bud Ridenour.

BJ-1 Duster sailplane.

BJ-1 Duster

BJ-1 Duster was designed by Ben Jansson, a Swedish sailplane enthusiast, and H. Finar Thor, a graduate aeronautical engineer, using the all-wood technique pioneered by Gus Briegleb. Main spar is built up from tapered spruce laminations. Dive brakes on the trailing edge are operated by torque tubes for good glide path control.

The wings are covered with 3/32 inch plywood, except for a fabric area on the outer panels between 45 and 75 percent of chord. The wing was designed to be built in three 18-foot sections for easier handling. A 10-inch go-kart landing wheel is mounted forward of the CG. This permits the sailplane to rest on its tailwheel. It can be flown with or without the canopy.

Span is 42 feet 8 inches; wing area is 104.65 square feet; aspect ratio 17.4. Emtpy weight is 390 pounds. Minimum sink is 2.5 fps @ 45 mph; placard airspeed, smooth air 128 mph. Needle-ball-airspeed, variometer, and sensitive altimeter permit cloud flying. Contact: DSK Aircraft Corp., 13161 Sherman Way, North Hollywood, CA 91605.

BJ-1 Duster cockpit.

Bowers Fly Baby.

Bowers Fly Baby

The single-place, wooden Fly Baby ultralight, low-wing monoplane was designed and built by Peter M. Bowers of Seattle, Washington, as an entry in a design competition of the Experimental Aircraft Association for a low-cost airplane suitable for inexperienced homebuilders to construct. It first flew on July 27, 1960, powered with a Continental A65 engine.

Following a crash, a new fuselage was fitted and a new engine was installed—a Continental C75 mod-

ified to develop 85 hp. This Fly Baby won the EAA competition in 1962. More than one hundred are now flying, including conversions to biplane and floatplane configurations.

With the 85-hp engine the Fly Baby has a V_{max} of 120 mph, cruises at 105 to 110 mph, climbs 1100 fpm, and has a range of 320 miles. It weighs only 605 pounds empty. Contact: Peter Bowers, 10458 16th Avenue South, Seattle, WA 98168.

Fly Baby panel.

Briegleb BG-12-16 sailplane.

Briegleb BG-12-16

Gus Briegleb, a World War II glider pilot instructor, founded a lovely soaring site at El Mirage Dry Lake north of Los Angeles, and there designed, built, and flew a series of soaring craft. In 1956 he designed the BG-12, a sailplane with a 50-foot span and 141 square feet of wing area that weighed 525 pounds empty.

Over the years improvements were made in a new model, the BG-12-16, which uses the BG-12 wing and has a low-profile fuselage. Fin and rudder sweep forward and an all-flying stabilator fitted with servo tabs was added. The BG-12-16 can be built in under 1000 man hours.

Briegleb loves to soar in the Sierra Wave when storm fronts blow across the California mountain range. To make the experience more comfortable, he designed the cockpit of the BG-12-16 so that he could stretch out, feet forward, thus increasing the headroom as well.

Gus Briegleb stretches out in cockpit.

Mustang 2.

Bushby Mustang 2

The Bushby M-II Mustang 2 is a two-place derivative of the single-seat Midget Mustang, designed by Robert Bushby of Route 1, Box 13B, Minooka, Illinois 60447. It was designed after the Midget Mustang's original designer, Piper's chief test pilot Dave Long, was killed in a flight test accident. Although it is a taildragger, an alternate tricycle gear may be used.

Intended as a fast cross-country and sport plane, the Mustang 2 has room for full IFR instrumentation in the roomy side-by-side cockpit. It normally uses a 160-hp Lycoming 0-320 flat-four engine that gives it a V_{max} of 204 mph, a best cruise of 201 mph, climb of 1400 fpm, 18,000 foot ceiling and 430-mile range. Contact: Robert Bushby, Route 1, Box 13B, Minooka, IL 60447.

Panel of Mustang 2.

Verne Menzimer's Cavalier SA 102.5.

Cavalier SA 102.5

Slide into the left seat of the sleek, low-wing Cavalier SA 102.5, strap your girl friend in the right seat, fire up, and head for the high sky! If you're flying with Verne Menzimer from Oceanside, California, where he hangars his prize-winning Cavalier, he'll spread a Naugahyde plastic-coated fabric panel on the seat for you to step on.

Settled down, you see a waterfall switch panel above the power console, with master, navigation, and instrument lights, etc., in a neat row. A single NAV/COMM Escort 110 is mounted above the panel.

Engine gauges are at right; flight dials are at left. A turn and bank at top center is flanked by sensitive altimeter and airspeed. The VSI is directly beneath it. A G-meter, clock, and magnetic compass complete the flight stuff.

Menzimer installed a 125-hp converted Lycoming GPU that gives him a cruise of 150 mph TAS with a 64-inch pitch prop. The wing is wooden, fabric covered behind the main spar and highly finished. The Cavalier weighs 970 pounds empty. His plans came from K&S Aircraft, 4623 Fortune Road S.E., Calgary, Alberta, Canada.

Cavalier cockpit shows 160 mph IAS cruise.

Cook JC-1 Challenger.

Cook JC-1 Challenger

Cook Aircraft Corporation was founded in 1968 to develop and market the JC-1 Challenger four-seat light aircraft designed by the late John Cook. Income from sale of plans for a homebuilt version was insufficient to cover expenses and the firm went bankrupt. The remaining prototype (N123CA) was sold. The static test airplane was broken up. All drawings and the remaining tooling are in the possession of John Parker of Rancho Palos Verdes, CA.

An all-metal, low-wing, high-performance cruiser, the JC-1 had been intended as a competitor to Piper, Cessna, Beech, and Grumman, as a low-cost, easy-to-fly and safe family plane. Cook was killed in a flight test maneuver during spin tests, but Parker escaped.

The JC-1 uses the 150-hp Lycoming 0-320-E2A and has 20-gallon fuel tanks in each wing for maximum range cruise of 600 miles. The gear is fixed. Maximum cruise is 145 mph; stall is 54 mph.

Panel of Cook Challenger.

Corben Baby Ace of 1930s.

Corben Baby Ace

In 1931 a midwesterner named Ace Corben founded the Corben Sport Plane & Supply Company at Peru, Indiana, to build and sell partly built construction kits for his parasol monoplane, the Baby Ace. In 1953 the Baby Ace was completely redesigned by Paul H. Poberezny, now president of the Experimental Aircraft Association. Plans were published in *Popular Mechanics* magazine, and soon hundreds of Baby Aces were flying, along with the EAA.

The original EAA Baby Ace today is displayed in their Air Museum at Hales Corners, Wisconsin. In 1976 I saw my first Baby Ace at Mojave Airport.

Owned by Bob Upton, it had been rebuilt by him. A Continental A65 engine replaced the Szekeley SR-3, a 3-cylinder, 45-horsepower radial, that powered the original.

I flew Upton's Baby Ace and found it delightful. I shot a picture of the instrument panel flying at 2100 feet. The airspeed indicated 89 mph at 2300 rpm. The Baby Ace panel is neat and adequate for VFR flying only, with an Escort 110 NAV/COMM radio under the panel. Airspeed indicator is at left; ball-bank indicator is at right; and the magnetic compass is at top center. Contact: Ace Aircraft Mfg. Co., 106 Arthur Road, Asheville, N.C. 22806.

Single cockpit of Corben Baby Ace.

Druine D-31 Turbulent.

Druine D-31 Turbulent

The original D-31 Turbulent was designed by the late Roger Druine, a French airman who designed his first homebuilt at the age of 17. In 1957 Rollason Aircraft & Engines Co. of England began manufacturing Turbulents and components for homebuilders. The Rollason-Turbulent first flew on January 1, 1958.

In 1972 a modified Turbulent built by Larry Weishar of Springfield, IL, won the EAA award for Most Beautiful VW-Powered Airplane at their annual Oshkosh Fly-In. Plans for the Turbulent are now available from Sturgeon Air Ltd., 30 Airport Road, Edmonton, Alberta, Canada.

The stock Turbulent, built from Sturgeon plans, weighs 342 pounds and was meant to use the VW engines of 25 to 36 hp, although larger powerplants have been installed. The Weishar Turbulent uses the 1200cc VW of 33 hp. He gets a V_{max} of 101 mph, cruises at 93 and flies in ground effect at 49.

Turbulent cockpit.

Dragonfly.

Dragonfly

Winner of the Experimental Aircraft Association's Outstanding New Design Award at Oshkosh in 1980, the two-place canard-type Dragonfly indirectly owes its origin to Burt Rutan, who initially evolved the unique planform and adapted it to the Quickie composite homebuilt.

Designed and built by Bob Walters, Dragonfly is powered with the 1600cc VW engine that gives it a top speed of 150 mph and a cruise of around 140. Estimated range is 500 miles. Wingspan is 22 feet; canard span is 20 feet; and total lifting area is 97 sq/ft. Dragonfly weighs 590 pounds empty and 1075 pounds gross.

The cockpit width of Dragonfly is 43 inches, similar to that of the Cessna 172. A wrist stick is installed at center, below centrally mounted flight instruments. The developers, Viking Aircraft, plan to investigate installation of the bigger 1835cc VW engine for high density-altitude operation. Cost to build is said to be around $5000. Contact: Viking Aircraft, 16551 Perdido Key Drive, Pensacola, FL 32507.

Dragonfly cockpit.

JD-2 Dyke Delta.

Dyke Delta

After an initial prototype, the JD-1, was destroyed in a fire, John W. Dyke of Fairborn, Ohio, built the four-place JD-2 Dyke Delta with a 22-foot wingspan and a 200-hp Lycoming 0-360 engine. It first flew in July, 1966. Tricycle gear is manually retracted. Some 300 are now being built. The second to fly was John Thompson's of Tuscon AZ, who also used the 200-hp Lycoming.

The wing uses a modified NACA 63012 and 66015 airfoil with no dihedral nor incidence. Center-section sweepback is 61 degrees, outer wing panel sweep is 31 degrees. Structure is of welded steel tubing. Laminated fiberglass skin is riveted on. Trailing edge elevons stretch across two-thirds of the span.

Using the 180-hp Lycoming 0-360, the Delta, which weighs 960 pounds empty, has a V_{max} of 190 mph, cruise of 180 mph, range of 720 miles at 155 mph economy cruise, 2000 fpm climb, and a service ceiling of 18,000 feet. Contact: John Dyke, 2840 Old Yellow Springs Road, Fairborn, OH 45325.

Dyke Delta panel.

Bill America's EAA Nesmith Cougar.

EAA Nesmith Cougar

Designed by Robert Nesmith, the prototype two-place, side-by-side high-wing monoplane called Cougar first flew in 1957. Since 1977 plans have been available from the Experimental Aircraft Association. Today an estimated 250 are flying. The Cougar closely resembles Steve Wittman's fine Tailwind but is a bit smaller and lighter in weight, although it has the same squared fuselage profile and constant chord wing.

The Cougar owned by Bill America of Gold Beach, Oregon, is heavier than most, at 810 pounds empty versus 624 pounds, but it carries a 125-hp GPU engine instead of the smaller 115 hp Lycoming 0-235

in most others. Like the Tailwind, the Cougar has rearward-swept landing gear legs.

Standard Cougars have room for 90 pounds of baggage behind the dual seats. The braced wooden wings are plywood covered except for fabric along the trailing edge. Fuselage is of steel tube construction, as are the tail feathers. Both are fabric covered. Bill America uses a Mark-3 Omnigator NAV/COMM. Above the flight instruments at left panel, he mounted a stopwatch for precision DR navigation and instrument approaches. Contact: Experimental Aircraft Assn. P.O. Box 229, Hales Corners, WI 53130.

Cruising at 140 mph IAS at 4500 feet.

Evans VP-2.

Evans VP-2

W. S. (Bud) Evans, a San Diego aerospace engineer, started off with the single-place VP-1 for the novice homebuilder as an easy to construct and safe to fly all-wooden aircraft. Appearance and performance were considered second to these aims. Two years of spare-time design and another year building was spent on the VP-1.

Next, Evans turned to development of a side-by-side two-seat version, the VP-2, generally similar to the single-place model but powered with a converted 40-hp VW engine. Later he switched to a 2100cc Revmaster VW conversion. With a 60-hp powerplant, VP-2 has a V_{max} of 100 mph, cruises at 75 mph, and stalls at 45 mph. ROC is 500 fpm, ceiling 10,000 feet, range 200 miles. Contact: Evans Aircraft, P.O. Box 744, La Jolla, CA 92038.

VP-2 cockpit.

Flying Flea.

Flying Flea

The Flying Flea was born in 1933 when Henri Mignet of France brought out his tandem-wing ultralight *Pou du Ciel* (Flying Flea). It created considerable controversy, with a reputation for being temperamental. After World War II, Mignet brought out Model HM-290 with a 25-hp Poinsard engine, which flew in 1958. Other models developed around this time were the HM-293, using the 30-hp VW engine, and HM-296 with the 40-hp Salmson engine.

The HM-350 series that followed was larger, with a 90-hp Continental C90-12F in the prototype that first flew in 1957. From this came the HM-380, a side-by-side two-seater with the 65-hp Continental and the three-seat HM-390 with a 90-hp engine. The Flying Flea replaces aileron and elevator control with a unique variable-incidence front wing. The Mignet HM-350 cruises at 105 mph, has a V_{max} of 130 mph, 13,000-foot ceiling, and a 500-mile range. Contact: Phil Howell, Rt. 4 Box 964, Christiansburg, VA 24073.

Flying Flea cockpit.

Hollmann HA-2M Sportster.

Hollmann HA-2M Sportster

Martin Hollmann, of Cupertino, CA, designed and built the world's first two-place gyroplane. It was designed for the homebuilder with limited access to power tools: 90 percent of the structure is bolted or riveted together and a minimum of machined parts are employed. The Sportster is designed to be road-towed to and from the flying site.

Powered with a rear-mounted Lycoming 0-320 of 150 hp, the Sportster uses a free-turning, two-bladed aluminum rotor of NACA 8-H-12 airfoil section, with a rotor prespin drive. The HA-2M can accelerate from a dead stop to 45 mph for takeoff within 350 to 500 feet and has a zero landing ground roll. V_{max} is 90 mph; cruise is 75 mph; and minimum mph is 28. Climb rate is 500 fpm; range is 90 miles. Contact: Hollman Aircraft, 11082 Bel Aire Court, Cupertino, CA 95014.

HA-2M Sportster panel.

Hovey Beta Bird.

Hovey Beta Bird

Aerospace Engineer Bob Hovey designed and built an ultralight biplane called the Whing Ding back in 1970 and sold 6000 sets of plans. Then he turned his attention to building a little high-wing monoplane ultralight, the Beta Bird, which first flew in April 1979 at Mojave Airport, California. The name referred to a beta propeller he had under development for improved low-speed flight.

Beta Bird's control stick moves the ailerons differentially for roll control. A side lever works the full-span "drooperons" together to serve as flaps. A McCulloch 101 pusher engine on the Whing Ding was replaced in Beta Bird with a converted 1385cc VW engine. Beta Bird weighs 405 pounds empty, can hit 85 mph, cruises at 80, and lands at 40. There's even a little gel-cell-powered radio in the dashboard. Contact: R. W. Hovey. P.O. Box 1074, Canyon Country, CA 91351.

Beta Bird panel.

Jaguar biplane.

Jaguar's cockpit.

Jaguar

Stavros Chrysostomides, of Columbia, South Carolina, a sculptor by profession, looked into the future of airplane design and saw a remarkable vision: forward-swept wings like those on the drawing boards of military fighter designers. Stavros felt they would offer a look of grace, plus better visibility, and so designed his biplane Jaguar accordingly.

In 19 months and 2000 man-hours of labor, he had the Jag ready for painting, then flying. With an 0-320 engine of 150 hp up front, the Jag hit 175 mph and cruised at 135.

Fuel capacity is 17 gallons in the mains plus another 5 gallons in a belly tank. Combined wing area is 93 sq/ft. Stavros was assisted in his homebuilt project by fellow members of the EAA Chapter 242 in Columbia. The Jaguar is the star of the show whenever it appears at EAA Fly-Ins.

Jeffair Barracuda.

Jeffair Barracuda

Design of the Barracuda began in August 1966. Prototype construction started in June 1969. First flight was made June 29, 1975. Barracuda is an all-wood, low-wing sport plane with retractable landing gear. A roomy cockpit for two seated side-by-side is covered with swing-up canopy.

Powered with a 220-hp G0-435-2 Lycoming flat four engine, Barracuda weighs 1495 pounds empty, cruises at 200 mph, and climbs at 2200 fpm. V_{max} is 218 mph. Designed and built by G. L. Siers of Bellevue, Washington, Barracuda features a wide, clean instrument panel with flight instruments grouped at left, engine instruments at right, NAV/COMM at center.

Below the panel between the seats is a flat panel for master switch, ignition switch, and fuel pump switch and a selector for either radio or tape deck. Visibility from the cockpit is excellent, and the cockpit is air-conditioned. Contact: Jeffair, P.O. Box 975, Renton, WA 98055.

Cockpit panel of Barracuda.

Jungster II.

Jungster II cockpit.

Jungster II

Los Angeles aeronautical engineer Rim Kaminskas in 1957 designed an agile aerobatic biplane, Jungster I, as an 8/10 scaled version of the famous Bucker Jungmeister, to preserve the excellent flying qualities of the Bucker. Kaminskas' second design, the Jungster II, was an outgrowth of this project. It was intended to retain the pleasure of flying an open cockpit sport plane with more speed for cross-country flying. It is a parasol type and has a larger cockpit with ample room for VFR/IFR radio gear and gauges.

Pilots say the Jungster II is highly sensitive. Turns can be made with rudder alone, an asset in executing snap rolls. Built of wood, like a model airplane on a bigger scale, the Jungster II, powered with a 125-hp CPU engine, can hit 170 mph, cruises at 148 mph, and stalls at 55. It climbs at 3500 fpm, gets off the grass in 200 feet, and lands in 800. Contact: K & S Aircraft, 4623 Fortune Road S.E., Calgary 23, Alberta, Canada.

Marquart MA5 Charger.

Marquart MA5 Charger

Ed Marquart's MA5 Charger biplane was completed in October 1970 as a fully aerobatic biplane stressed to +6 and −4.5 Gs and designed to use engines from 100 through 180 hp. The prototype uses a 125-hp Lycoming 0-290-1 engine and metal McCauley two-bladed propeller. It offers a V_{max} of 125 mph, cruise of 115 mph, and 1200 fpm ROC at 65 IAS.

Wingspan is 24 feet; length is 20½ feet; and wing area is 170 sq/ft. Wing sweepback is 10 degrees; dihedral and incidence, 1 degree upper, 2 degrees lower wing. Empty weight is 1035 pounds, gross weight 1600 pounds.

Charger is soloed from the rear seat where all the gauges are, so that flown either solo or dual, the CG is unaffected. Marquart's partner in the project was Dan Fielder. Contact: Ed Marquart, P.O. Box 3032, Riverside, CA 92509.

Marquart MA5 cockpits.

Mini Coupe.

Mini Coupe

Design of the Mini Coupe began in 1968, and first flight took place in September 1971. By 1975 some 150 sets of plans had been sold of which 26 are known to be flying. A lightweight, single-seat, all-metal sport plane, Mini Coupe is powered with a modified 1600cc VW engine of 65 hp, though the Continental A65 also may be installed.

The cockpit is open, but a canopy is optional. The baggage compartment is behind the headrest. In 1975, fiberglass wingtip extensions were added to increase the wing area from 79.8 sq/ft. to 83.5 sq/ft. Wingspan is 24 feet; length is 16 feet 4 inches; empty weight is 497 pounds; and gross weight is 850 pounds. Maximum speed is 105 mph; best cruise speed, 90 mph; climb, 750 fpm; range, 300 miles. Plans and kits are sold by Bill Johnson, P.O. Box 1, Hillsboro, OR 97123.

Mini Coupe cockpit.

Mitchell P-38 Lightning.

Mitchell P-38 Lightning

Named for the famous World War II Lockheed twin-boom P-38 Lightning, Mitchell Aircraft Corporation (1900 South Newcomb, Porterville, CA 93257) in 1981 developed an ultralight namesake weighing only 200 pounds, powered with a 250cc Honda Odyssey engine. The pilot rides out front in the open breeze at a 40-mph cruise, using a left-side wrist-stick and conventional rudders.

With a tricycle landing gear, the Mitchell P-38 gets off in 200 feet and lands in 100 feet, has a V_{max} of 60 mph, and a stall speed of 30 mph. It takes four people a single day to assemble this ultralight.

P-38's open cockpit.

PDQ-2 in flight.

PDQ-2 instrument panel.

PDQ-2

The PDQ-2 was designed to be an inexpensive, strong and easy-to-assemble homebuilt sport machine for the low-time pilot. Design began in 1972. The first flight was on May 30, 1973. The prototype was powered with a Rockwell (Venture) JL0-LB-600-2 two-cylinder engine, and later with the more easily available 1385cc VW engine conversion, or 1600cc VW.

With the latter powerplant, PDQ-2 weighs 320 pounds empty, and can fly 90 mph, cruise at 70, climb 500 fpm, stalls at 40 mph, gets off in 300 feet, and lands in 250.

Plans and kits are available from Wayne Ison, Route 6, Forrestwood Drive #9, Manchester, IN 37355.

Polliwagen in flight.

Polliwagen

Polliwagen is a clean, side-by-side, two-place sport plane with a low wing and T-tail powered with the 126-CID Revmaster R-2100D turbocharged VW-type engine, weighing 600 pounds empty and grossing 1250 pounds. With a wingspan of 26 feet and 90 square feet of wing area, its power loading is 14.5 lb/hp. Wing loading is 12.2 lb/sq ft. and span loading is 24.3 lb/sq ft. Flying at 80 percent power, Polliwagen has a ROC of 1000 fpm with two aboard or 1115 fpm flown solo. Cruise speed is advertised as 150 mph, but the designer, Joe Alvarez, says it will do 165 mph TAS at 2000 feet in cruise mode. Plans are available from Joe Alvarez, 8782 Hewitt Place, Garden Grove, CA 92644.

Panel of prototype Polliwagen.

Pazmany PL-4A.

Pazmany PL- 4A

The PL-4A was designed as an inexpensive. easy-to-build single-seater for homebuilders, with safety and economy of operation thrown in. The prototype first flew in July 1972. PL-4A's wings are foldable for road-towing and easy storage. It uses a modified 1600cc VW engine of 50 hp.

With a wingspan of 26 feet 8 inches and 89 sq/ft. of wing area, it weighs 578 pounds empty and 850 pounds loaded. The PL-4A has a V_{max} of 125 mph, cruises at 98 mph, climbs at 650 fpm, and has a 340-mile range. Construction is all-metal; the gear is non-retractable. For details write to the designer, Ladislao Pazmany, P.O. Box 80051, San Diego, CA 92138.

PL-4A cockpit.

Pitts S-1D.

Pitts S-1D

Curtis Pitts has now designed a complete line of fine aerobatic biplanes with addition of the S-1D homebuilders' project along with a kit version of the factory-built Model S-1S. The original single-seater Pitts Special, designed from 1943 to '44, first flew in September of '44. Bigger, more powerful engines are now installed for competition aerobatic flying.

Plans are available for the Pitts S-1D Special from P.O. Box 547, Afton, WY 83110. Kits also are available for this fine biplane, built of steel tubing, wood, and fabric. With a 260-hp engine the S-1D, which weighs 720 pounds empty, has a V_{ne} of 203 mph, cruises at 154 mph, climbs at 2640 fpm, and stalls at 57 mph.

Pitts S-1D cockpit.

Quickie.

Quickie

Quickie is a single-place, composite construction, canard-type homebuilt aircraft that offers a top speed of 150 mph behind an 18-hp Onan powerplant. The Quickie was designed by Burt Rutan and is marketed by Quickie Aircraft Corp., P.O. Box 786, Mojave, CA 93502. Both plans and materials kits are available.

Quickie cruises at 121 mph, climbs 425 fpm, stalls at 53 mph, gets off in 660 feet, and lands in 835 feet. Its ceiling is 13,000 feet; range is 750 miles.

Quickie's wingspan is 17 feet 8 inches. Wing area is 55 sq/ft.; empty weight is 240 pounds, gross weight is 480 pounds. It carries 8 gallons of fuel and 30 pounds of baggage. An interesting feature is the way the cockpit instruments swing open with the canopy during entry.

Quickie cockpit.

Q-2.

Q-2

Q-2 is a two-place version of the Quickie, with entirely new engineering but similar construction. Tom Jewett and Gene Sheehan of Quickie Aircraft Corp. (Hangar 28, Mojave, CA 93501) worked with a Canadian Quickie representative, Garry LeGare, in developing Q-2 in 1979. Tom and Gene did the design work, and Garry did the actual building of the prototype.

The Q-2 engine recommended is the Revmaster 2100-DQ, detuned to 64 hp from 85 hp for maximum reliability with the supercharger removed. With full electrical system and radio gear the empty weight is 537 pounds.

Performance is V_{max} 180 mph, cruise 165 climb 1000 fpm, range 750 miles, and takeoff distance 500 feet. Cost to build is $8995. Economy cruise range exceeds 1000 miles.

Q-2 cockpit.

Rand KR-1.

Rand KR-1 cockpit.

Rand KR-1

First flight of the Rand KR-1 was made in February, 1972 using a 1200cc VW conversion, later replaced by a 1700cc VW engine of 58 hp. A low-wing, retractable-gear single-seater, the KR-1 has a V_{max} of 170 mph, 155 mph cruise, 700 fpm climb rate, and 748 mile range.

Wing and fuselage are of composite construction, using wood spars, styrofoam ribs with spaces between filled with foam slabs covered with Dynel/epoxy. A spruce/plywood fuselage frame is covered with carved foam, which is Dynel/epoxy covered. More than 6000 sets of plans have been sold, of which more than 200 KR-1s flying.

The single-place cockpit is comfortable and has a side stick control with a panel ample to hold standard VFR/IFR gauges and NAV/COMM radio equipment. Contact: Rand Robinson Engineering, Inc., 5842-K McFadden Avenue, Huntington Beach, CA 92649.

KR-1B Motorglider.

Rand KR-1B Motorglider

The KR-1B Motorglider is a variant of the original KR-1 composite sport plane designed by the late Ken Rand of Huntington Beach, California. It has higher aspect ratio wings that may be retrofitted to the single-place KR-1 (but not to the two-place KR-2).

With a wingspan of 27 feet and 91 sq/ft. of wing area, the 484-pound (empty weight) KR-1B, which grosses 800 pounds, has a wing loading of 8.79:1 and a power loading as tested of 13.3:1. The prototype KR-1B uses the 1834cc VW conversion of 60 hp. The KR-1B's rudder is 4 inches wider than that of the KR-1 for better ground control in a crosswind.

Rand Robinson Engineering, Inc., of 5842-K McFadden Avenue, Huntington Beach, CA 92649, sells complete plans for $85 and advertises performance as: V_{ne} 144; maximum cruise 130; maneuvering speed 120; maximum flap extended speed 100; stall (spoiler flap extended) 45; stall (spoiler flap retracted) 38; takeoff 300 feet; land 300 feet; L/D 20:1.

Cockpit of KR-1B.

Rutan VariViggen.

Rutan VariViggen

The VariViggen prototype made its first flight in May, 1972 after development in model form with a "cartop wind tunnel" that proved its excellent anti-stall characteristics. The VariViggen can climb, cruise, glide turn and land with continuous full aft control stick with a stable 52 mph TAS throughout.

By using a canard surface up front, the Vari-Viggen has greater low-speed lift at low angle of attack, more positive lift control, and reduced trim and induced drag at higher speeds. The canard permits use of a controllable reflexed trailing edge of the main wing.

With the 150-hp Lycoming 0-320-A2A engine, VariViggen has a V_{max} of 163 mph, a 150-mph cruise, 1200 fpm ROC, and a 400-mile range. The two tandem seats are finished in leather and fur. For details write Rutan Aircraft Factory, P.O. Box 656, Mojave, CA 93501.

VariViggen cockpit.

Rutan VariEze.

Rutan VariEze

Burt Rutan called this design the VariEze because it is very easy to build and to fly. It differs from his earlier VariViggen in having more conventional swept wings of high aspect ratio, with NASA-designed Whitcomb winglets further to enhance its L/D performance by decreasing the vortex drag of the tips.

VariEze's main gear is fixed. The nose gear is retractable by means of a crank on the cockpit panel (see photo). It first flew in May 1975, and its original VW engine was switched to the reliable Continental 0-200 of 100 hp.

By 1981 an estimated 3000 VariEzes were under construction or flying the world over as homebuilders quickly turned to the advantages of composite construction of this unique design. The VariEze, a two-place tandem craft, has a cruise speed of over 200 mph max, or 145 mph in economy cruise mode. At 75 percent power, range is 700 miles. For plans or kits contact Rutan Aircraft Factory, P.O. Box 656, Mojave, CA 93501.

Prototype VariEze cockpit.

Rutan Long-EZ.

Rutan Long-EZ

Burt Rutan's new Long-EZ first flew with its finalized improved rear wing in October, 1979. The wing features less sweep, more area, a new airfoil, longer ailerons, an improved winglet juncture, and overlap-type wing attachment to center section spar which permits incidence adjustment. The design permits full stall landings with good forward visibility.

Rutan recommends the Long-EZ design for Continental 0-200 engines and Lycoming 0-235s, with ap-

proval for complete electrical systems including starter and night lights.

Rutan's brother, retired Col. Dick Rutan, USAF, set a world closed-course record flying the Long-EZ nonstop for 33 hours 33 minutes 44 seconds. Next, he set his sights on a round-the-world nonstop flight in Long-EZ. Modification kits for Long-EZ wings are available to VariEze owners from the Rutan Aircraft Factory, P.O. Box 656, Mojave, CA 93501.

Long-EZ cockpit.

Rutan RAF-40 Defiant.

Rutan RAF- 40 Defiant

RAF-40 is the 40th design of talented Burt Rutan of Mojave, California, conceived to bring added safety to the light-twin market through use of centerline thrust push-pull engines, lightweight composite construction, and other features. With one engine out there is no asymetrical thrust, and the Defiant can actually climb on one engine at gross weight if the other quits.

Powerplants are two Lycoming 0-320s of 160 hp, the aircraft profile flowing smoothly back with minimum drag. At 1500 pounds empty, the RAF-40's lightness is not due to composite construction (metal would be lighter), and the glass wings are super smooth.

Design stall speed is 61 knots; V_{max} 180k at 12,500 feet; range 1000 nm on 95 gallons; rate of climb 1600 fpm; single-engine ROC (dirty) 280 fpm. For information write Rutan Aircraft Factory, P.O. Box 656, Mojave, CA 93501.

RAF-40 cruising at 180 IAS @ 2050/2200.

Spencer Amphibian Air Car.

Spencer Amphibian Air Car

Percival H. Spencer, designer of the famous World War II Republic SeaBee, created that amphibian from a prior homebuilt design of his, the S-12 two-seat amphibian. After the war he further changed the original design into a four-place homebuilt amphibian, the Model S-12-E Air Car, using the Teledyne Continental Tiara Series 6-285-B flat-six engine of 280 hp.

The Air Car wing is of braced wood, steel and fiberglass, with fiberglass tip floats that serve as auxiliary fuel tanks. The hull is conventional construction with wooden frames, longerons, and skin. Wing and engine are hung on a welded steel tube cabane structure, with attachment points for the landing gear.

Weighing 2190 pounds empty and 3200 pounds gross, the Air Car has a V_{max} of 147 mph, 135-mph cruise, 43-mph stall, 1000 fpm climb, and 700-mile range. Contact: Spencer Amphibian Air Car, 12780 Pierce Street, Pacoima, CA 91331.

Passenger entering Air Car.

Stits Flut-R-Bug.

Stits Flut-R-Bug

In 1955 Stits Aircraft began development of component kits to be assembled by amateur aircraft builders into a tandem, two-place, mid-wing sport plane called the Flut-R-Bug SA-6A. This model was superceded by a second model, the SA-6B, with slightly increased empty and gross weights as was the fuel capacity. With wooden wings and a steel tube fuselage, the SA-6B became popular along with other Stit-designs such as the Playboy and Skycoupe.

Powered with the 65-hp Continental A65 four-cylinder air-cooled engine, the Flut-R-Bug has a V_{max} of roughly 100 mph, cruise of 90 mph, 1000-fpm climb and 260-mile range. Empty weight is 575 pounds, or 1031 pounds loaded. Wingspan is 26 feet; length, 18 feet; and wing area, 130 sq/ft. The wings have full-span, narrow-chord ailerons. (Stits no longer sells plans for Flut-R-Bug.)

Flut-R-Bug cockpit.

Steen Skybolt.

Steen Skybolt

Lamar Steen of Brighton, Colorado, designed the two-seat aerobatic Skybolt. Simplicity of construction was his primary goal. The prototype was built as a class project in a Denver high school, where he instructed in an aerospace program. Design work began in 1968; construction took place in 1969. Cost to build was about $5000, and first flight took place in October, 1970. More than 1000 sets of plans have now been sold, and many fine Skybolts are flying.

One example is N52DH, a Skybolt built by Dr. Dean Hall of Fullerton, California, who fully equipped his biplane with IFR instruments and radio and enjoys flying it in any kind of weather. Skybolt weighs 1080 pounds empty, grosses 1800 pounds, has a V_{max} of 145 mph, and cruises at 130. With a 180-hp Lycoming IO-360, Skybolt climbs at 2500 fpm. For plans and kits write to Steen Aero Lab, 15263 De Gaulle Circle, Brighton, CO 80601.

Steen Skybolt panel.

Stolp Acroduster Too.

Stolp Acroduster Too SA750

Acroduster Too began as a scaled-down version of the Starduster Too SA300. It is powered with a 200-hp I0-360 Lycoming modified for full inverted flight. About 9/10 the size of Lou Stolp's Starduster Too SA-300, Acroduster Too was developed by airline pilot Morgan Schrack for competition flying, with bigger ailerons for a faster roll rate and stressed to +9 Gs.

With the front cockpit covered and using the big 200-hp engine, the SA750 will climb at 2300 fpm, top 200 mph, cruise at 160 mph, and stall at 55 mph. The NACA 63012 symmetrical wings provide excellent handling from V_{max} down to stall. The empty weight is 1000 pounds; gross weight is 1630 pounds. Plans and kits are available from Stolp Starduster Corp., 4301 Twining Street, Riverside, CA 92509.

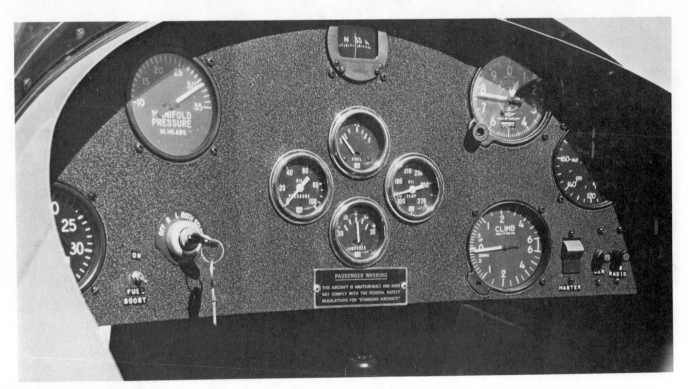

Acroduster Too cockpit.

Stolp SA-500 Starlet.

Stolp SA-500 Starlet

Baby of the Stolp aircraft family is the SA-500 Starlet parasol monoplane. It was originally designed to take a VW engine conversion but is now usually powered with bigger engines up to 125 hp (the engine in N190TF pictured here is a Continental of 85 hp).

Inherently stable and designed to operate from rough fields, the little Starlet has a fuselage of steel tubing, fabric covered; the wing is of spruce spars and plywood ribs of the Clark Y airfoil. N190TF, built by Terry Fox of Hawthorne, California, has a V_{max} of 130 mph, 75 percent power cruise of 105 mph, and stalls at 50 mph. Its ROC is 1500 fpm at 80 mph IAS.

Plans, kits, and materials are available to homebuilders from Stolp Starduster Corp., 4301 Twining Street, Riverside, CA 92509.

SA-500 cockpit.

Turner T-40B.

Turner T-40B

Eugene L. Turner, an FAA crash survival specialist, designed and first flew his original T-40 single-seater in April 1961. Since then he has developed a series including the T-40A, Super T-40A, T-40B, and T-40C. The T-40 won the 1961 EAA Outstanding Design Trophy. After collecting 18 awards Turner split it down the middle and enlarged it to a two-placer, the T-40A.

The T-40B is basically the same as the T-40A but has a tricycle landing gear and other changes. A 125-hp engine replaces the original 85-hp powerplant. The T-40C uses a computer-developed version of the NASA GA(W)-2 supercritical wing.

The T-40B shown here uses the NACA 64212 airfoil with double-slotted flaps, and with 125 hp has a V_{max} of 175 mph, cruises at 155 mph, stalls at 57 mph. Range is 475 miles. Contact: Turner Educational Development Enterprises (TEDDE), P.O. Box 425, Stratford, CT 06497.

T-40B cockpit.

Teenie Two.

Teenie Two

One of the tiniest homebuilts flying today is the all-metal, single-place, low-wing Teenie Two that measures less than 13 feet in length. In 1971, *Popular Mechanics* featured the Teenie Two as a follow-on to the earlier Jeanie's Teenie, for which 7000 sets of plans were sold.

Designed by Calvin Parker, Teenie Two weighs only 310 pounds empty or 590 pounds gross weight. Using a 53-hp 1500cc VW engine, it lifts off at 50 mph, climbs at 800 fpm, cruises at 110 mph on 75 percent power, and has a V_{max} of 120 mph. The tricycle landing gear uses rubber hose as shock absorbers. Contact: C. Y. Parker, P.O. Box 625, Coolidge, AZ 85228.

Teenie Two cockpit.

John Thorp and the T-18.

Thorp T-18 Tiger

John Thorp, an aerospace engineer, founded the Thorp Engineering Company to market plans for his T-18 Tiger. The prototype, built by Bill Warwick, used an 0-360 180-hp Lycoming and first flew on May 12, 1964. The T-18 pictured is owned by Mr. Thorp.

Lou Sunderland subsequently designed a folding-wing modification that is now offered by Ken Knowles Sport Aircraft, Inc. (5398 Trail Street, Norco, CA 91760) along with complete T-18 kits. The T-18 is the "Rolls Royce" of homebuilts, an all-metal, low-wing side-by-side two-seater with clean aerodynamic lines that give it exceptional performance. V_{max} is over 200 mph; cruise is 175 mph; climb rate is 2000 fpm; ceiling is 20,000 feet; and range is 500 miles.

Thorp T-18 panel.

Pappy Boyington flying RV-3.

Van's RV-3

Richard Van Gruneven's all-metal, single-place sport monoplane RV-3 won the EAA 1972 Award for Best Aerodynamic Detailing. Wings are constructed around a single I-beam spar and a lighter rear spar. Fuselage and empennage are metal construction, and the engine uses a fiberglass cowling.

The RV-3 dates back to 1968. Construction took 2½ years and cost $2000. In addition to trailing edge flaps, RV-3 uses drooping ailerons for improved low-speed control. Powerplant is the 125-hp Lycoming 0-290-G, providing a V_{max} of 195 mph, best cruise of 185 mph, 1900 fpm climb, 21,000-foot ceiling, 600-mile range. Former USMC pilot Gregory (Pappy) Boyington is one of more than 400 RV-3 builders and checked out in the prototype N17RV.

A wide-gear taildragger, RV-3 is easy to handle on the ground and a delight to fly in normal aerobatics. Plans and kits are available from Van's Aircraft, 22730 S.W. Francis, Beaverton, OR 97005.

RV-3 cockpit.

Volmer VJ-22 Sportsman.

Volmer VJ-22 Sportsman

Volmer Jensen designed and built the prototype VJ-22 Sportsman light amphibian, which first flew on December 22, 1958, and has since logged several thousand hours in the air. The two-place Sportsman amphibian is built largely of wood with metal ribs. The wooden hull structure is skinned with plywood and fiberglass. Gear is retractable.

More than 100 VJ-22 Sportsman amphibians are now flying, and close to 1000 sets of plans have been sold by Mr. Jensen (P.O. Box 5222, Glendale, CA 91201). The prototype uses a Continental C85 engine of 85 hp. Empty weight is 1000 pounds; gross weight is 1500 pounds. V_{max} is 95 mph, cruise is 85 mph; climb rate is 600 fpm; and range is 300 miles.

VJ-22 Sportsman cockpit.

Wendt Traveler.

WH-1 Wendt Traveler

The Wendt Traveler is the design of the late Harold O. Wendt, a former Convair aerospace engineer of San Diego who was killed in a plane crash in 1977. Like Bud Evans, a fellow aircrafter who designed the VP-1 and VP-2 for easy construction, Wendt shot for simplicity but better cross-country performance.

The result was an excellent tandem two-seater with a low wing, constructed of wood, offering low frontal area for better speed behind a Continental A65 engine of 65 hp. Empty weight including starter, alternator and radios is 900 pounds; useful load is 500 pounds.

With 22 gallons of fuel the Traveler has a range close to 500 miles. It cruises at 120 mph at 3000 feet MSL, stalls at 65, and climbs at 500 fpm. A clean instrument panel offers easy scanning, with long "picture windows" of the canopy providing excellent visibility from both front and rear seats.

Cockpit of Wendt Traveler.

Wittman Tailwind.

Wittman W-8 Tailwind

Noted racing pilot Steve Wittman has designed a large number of homebuilts. The most popular was his W-8 Tailwind. The prototype was built from 1952 to 53 and proved so successful that huge demands were made for sets of plans and prefabricated components. Hundreds are flying.

Like John Thorp's T-18, the Tailwind has a squarish fuselage for easy construction, but materials are wood-and-fabric wings and a fabric-covered steel tubing fuselage, with a tailwheel landing gear. Powered with a Continental 0-200 engine of 100 hp, the Tailwind has a V_{max} of 165 mph, cruises at 160 mph, climbs at 900 fpm, and has a 600-mile range. Two people sit side by side, with room for 60 pounds of baggage behind the seats. Contact Steve Wittman, P.O. Box 2762, Oshkosh, WI 54901 for plans.

Tailwind cockpit.

Woody's Pusher.

Woody's Pusher

Inspired by the lovely, ancient CW-1 Curtiss-Wright Junior, the late Harris L. Woods designed a homebuilt version. Today more than 100 are either under construction or flying. The craft is a tandem two-seater with a parasol wing powered with engines from 65 to 85 hp.

With an empty weight of 630 pounds and 1150 pounds gross, Woody's Pusher has a V_{max} of 98 mph, cruises at 87 mph, climbs 600 fpm, and stalls at 45 mph. It gets off in 300 feet, lands in 400, and has a range of 225 miles. Plans are available from Mrs. Eva Woods, 3715 Greenleaf Street, Raleigh, N.C. 27606.

Panel of Woody's Pusher.

Zenith CH-200.

Zenith CH-200

French-born designer Chris Heintz, former chief designer at Avions Pierre Robin, a leading lightplane maker, moved to Toronto, Canada, and brought with him plans to develop a homebuilt plane he had created in France. A two-place, side-by-side low-wing monoplane with tricycle gear, the CH-200 first flew in October 1968 in France.

The design goal was an easy-to-build all-metal monoplane that would be efficient to fly, with electrically operated flaps and able to take engines from 85 to 160 hp. Both vertical and horizontal tail surfaces are all-moving. With a 100-hp Continental 0-200 engine, the CH-200 weighs 890 pounds empty, 1440 pounds gross, has a V_{max} of 145 mph, cruises at 127 mph, stalls at 53 mph dirty, and has a 500-mile range. Contact: Zenair Ltd., 236 Richmond Street, Richmond Hill, Ontario, Canada L4C 3Y8.

Cockpit of CH-200.

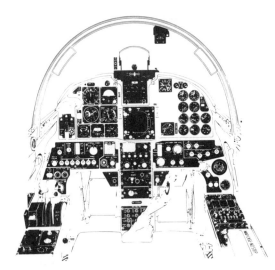

Chapter 8

General Aviation Cockpits

The Federal Aviation Administration, in a 1981-1982 Aviation Forecast noted significant changes in General Aviation flying, with emphasis on the rise in use of aircraft for business travel, as measured by the growth pattern in the GA fleet, aircraft sales, and total hours flown. At the end of 1979 there were 208,000 aircraft in the GA fleet; 6400 were turboprop and jet fixed-wing aircraft. Orders for these were backlogged up to three years, while production of many smaller aircraft was suspended for periods in 1980. Sales of heavier, more sophisticated aircraft were predominantly for business use, says the FAA.

An equally significant trend serving as an indicator of General Aviation's changing character was the growing percentage of pilots who possess instrument ratings. As of January 1, 1980, 247,100 of 604,500 licensed pilots (41 percent) were instrument rated, compared with 32 percent in 1970.

In its June 1980 issue of *AOPA Pilot*, the Aircraft Owners and Pilots Association's Associate Editor Mark M. Lacagnina introduced their 1980 Avionics Directory and Buyers' Guide by pointing out that "Advances in technology have brought the size and weight of avionics down to levels at which the panels of almost every lightplane can be filled with the required instruments for IFR flight."

However, despite the pioneering of electronic displays by such craft as the NASA Space Shuttle Columbia and the new-generation Boeing 757 and 767, as well as Lockheed's L-1011-500 and other modern aircraft, "it may be some time before 'glass' cockpits are widely used in General Aviation aircraft," says AOPA. While GA pilots may get excited about the wonders of CRT (Cathode Ray Tube) technology, what they really seek is reliability.

Dual Radios

Rather than going to the expense of installing expensive, sophisticated new equipment, the GA pilot is more likely to want to install less-expensive dual radios, so that if one konks out, he has a redundant unit for backup. Furthermore, because of high interest rates and fuels costs, aircraft owners are more and more reequipping their older aircraft with modern cockpit instrumentation, rather than buying complete new aircraft.

One trend AOPA noted was toward the use of lighter materials in cockpit equipment construction, rather than making the black boxes and gauges smaller and smaller. Charles Husick, senior vice president of Cessna's Aircraft Radio and Control Division, observed: "Pilot's eyes are not getting any more acute, and their fingers are not getting any smaller, so the characteristics of the human being are going to put a bottom limit on how small units can get."

Reliability of today's avionics equipment is being enhanced by introduction of digital technology, providing new ways of processing electronic signals and presenting the information to the General Aviation pilot. Says AOPA: "Light bars and digital readouts are becoming common means of presenting information to the pilot."

Herb Sawinski, PR manager for Bendix Avionics Division, points out that "Our General Aviation radar can display everything except attitude on electronic cockpit displays. We can display checklists, moving maps, and either VOR or area navigation . . . you're limited only by your imagination in what you can do with digital technology."

There's even talk, says Sawinski, of avionics that obey voice commands instead of manual tuning—simply say ONE-TWO-ONE-POINT-SIX instead of turning a dial to 121.6 and your radio tunes itself to the frequency.

While General Aviation probably will not get around to installing CRT technology for many years to come, prices for sure will drop with increased demand, as with video recorders and other home electronics devices that are coming in the mass market.

Twenty years ago, says Edward King, chairman of King Radio Corporation, "none of our aircraft had distance measuring equipment (DME); it was just being developed. The airlines had just started using DME, but not until around 1963-64 did DME enter the light aircraft field."

VOR/DME RNAV

General Aviation has been out in front in another area of modern avionics, says King, in use of VOR/DME-type Area Navigation. If you can afford DME you're likely to install RNAV. Less financially secure plane owners manage to navigate by radio across country minus DME, simply using a dual VOR installation, which takes a tiny bit longer to plot position.

Remote-type equipment also is down the line for the General Aviation pilot who now flies by gyro gauges installed right in the instrument panel, sometimes mechanically linked to present heading and attitude readouts. This is fine for single engine air-

craft, but it gets more complex in multi-engine craft where you want to go to Flight Directors that give you computed pitch, bank, and roll commands.

Right after World War II, a careful pilot/shopper could run down to the war surplus store and pick up a used military directional gyro, artificial horizon, radio compass, or even a Norden bombsight for peanuts, but today gyro instruments generally aren't cheap.

You can also spend up to $62,000 for Area Navigation units, $20,000 for encoding altimeters, or $10,000 for DME equipment. But, you can shop around and fill your panel with avionics units for a tenth of those prices, or whatever your pocketbook can stand.

Many General Aviation pilots complain that the FAA is hogging the sky with more and more restricted areas that require super-sophisticated equipment to fly through, but there are still vast horizons of wide open spaces where the Piper Cub driver can legally get around the way the Wright Brothers did—with a string on a wing!

*Model 17 Beechcraft
Staggerwing.*

Beech Model 17 Staggerwing

On November 14, 1932, in the midst of the Great
Depression, the first Beechcraft Model 17 Staggerwing biplane made its maiden flight to Wichita. It
showed a top speed of more than 200 mph, a cruise of
180 mph, landing speed of 60 mph, ROC of 1600 fpm,
and ceiling of 21,500 feet. Initial production models
came off the line the following year as the Model 17R
(420-hp Whirlwind) and the A17F (700-hp Cyclone)
with fixed gear, and the B17L (255-hp Jacobs) with
retractable undercarriage.

A total of 424 Model 17s had been built when
World War II began and when 207 Staggerwings were
delivered to the USAAF as UC-43s and 63 were delivered to the Navy as GB-1s. Production was resumed
in 1945 with the five-seater G17S, and 90 were built
before production ended. The typical Beech G17S carried the 450 hp Pratt & Whitney R-985 Wasp Junior.

In 1936 Louise Thaden flew a Beechcraft C17R in
the Bendix Race, from Bendix, New Jersey, to Los
Angeles, to win with a transcontinental speed record
for women pilots in 14 hours 55 minutes 1 second.

Cockpit of Beechcraft Staggerwing.

Model 18 Twin Beech prototype of 1937. (courtesy Beech)

Beech Model 18

When the last three Beechcraft Super H18s were delivered to Japan Air Lines on November 26, 1969, the world's longest continuous aircraft production run came to an end. First flown in January, 1937, more than 7000 Model 18s were built in 32 variations over 32 years. A standard of business aviation, the soundness of the Twin Beech's design is evident in such areas as a 3200 pound increase in gross weight and resultant payload boost, a 40-mph rise in cruising speed,

steady improvement in reliability, and adaptability to countless special missions.

There was little market among airlines in the United States for the Twin Beech in the late '30s; the major airlines required larger equipment, while the smaller feeder lines were yet to develop. In Canada, however, feeder lines regularly served territories located off the main transcontinental rail and air routes, and some of the first Model 18s were used in this

Cockpit of Model 18 prototype. (courtesy Beech)

Beechcraft Model Super H18 of 1969. (courtesy Beech)

service, equipped for interchangeable operation from skis or float landing gear. The Twin Beech also found favor among corporate and private customers.

By the start of World War II, 39 Model 18s had been sold. During the war, Beech produced 5257 modified Model 18s for Allied military forces for training pilots, gunners, and navigators, and for transporting priority military cargo throughout the world. These 18s carried such designations as C-45, AT-7, AT-11, and F-2 for the Army Air Corps, JRB and SNB for the Navy, and Expeditor for the Royal Canadian Air Force. It is estimated that over 90 percent of American bombardiers and navigators who saw service in World War II trained in military versions of the Twin Beech. The last Air Force C-45s were phased out in 1963, and the Navy retired its last SNB-5 in 1972.

Postwar development included the Model D18S, which featured flush riveting and a 20 percent increase in gross weight with improved range and payload; the Model D18C for feeder airlines; and the E18S, which featured greater cabin area through an increase in fuselage height, added wing area, and increased performance.

Addition of tricycle landing gear through use of the Volpar modification kit and an extended nose section was offered by Beech as a factory-installed option beginning early in the Super H18 series of 1962. The Super H18 was powered by 450-hp Pratt & Whitney R-985 engines with three-blade, full-feathering propellers. Top speed was 235 mph, high cruise speed was 220 mph, and range was over 1500 miles.

Cockpit of Beech Super H18. (courtesy Beech)

Model V-35 Beech Bananza.

Beech Model V-35 Bonanza

The V-tail design was conceived in 1943 when Beech experimented with the design on an AT-10 for possible military use. It proved to have superior spin recovery capability and less wetted surface that a conventional empennage design. The first Bonanza to fly used a laminar flow wing and Lycoming G0-290 engine of 165 hp. Later a switch was made to the NACA 23000 series wing and 165-hp Continental engine.

Aside from a tendency of the V-35 to hunt a bit, flying this model is sheer delight, with a max cruise of 175 mph, 750-mile range, and 18,000-foot ceiling. By 1975 a total of 10,000 Bonanzas had been built (the 10,000th was a Model V-35B V-tailed version). In 1960, a straight-tailed version, the Debonair, appeared.

Jerry Coigny, a retired airline pilot, lives on a ranch in the Sierra Nevadas of California and owns his own airstrip, high on a 4100-foot elevation hogback. There he keeps his sleek little 1947 Model V-35 Beech Bonanza in mint condition. On holidays he tours the entire country with his pretty wife Lucy.

Note the swing-over control column in Coigny's 1947 Bonanza whose cockpit is immaculate, as if it just came from the factory.

Cockpit of Jerry Coigny's V-35 Bonanza.

Beech C23 Sundowner.

Beech C23 Sundowner

The Beech C23 Sundowner is one of three aircraft renamed in 1971 from previous Musketeer designations, along with the Sport B19 and Sierra A24R. The 150-hp Sport is the smallest of the line. The Sundowner is in the middle, with the Lycoming 0-360-A4K of 180 hp, and then comes the 4-6 place Sierra.

Like Sport and Sierra, the four-place Sundowner has both left and right doors. Its gear is fixed, with a wide 12-foot tread. The nosewheel is steerable and self-centering. The wing is of NACA 632A415 airfoil, constant chord with two-degree tip washout, providing excellent slow-flight handling. Passengers have three picture windows along each side of the cabin.

Panel layout is standard with flight instruments at left, engine gauges at center, and the radio stack at right. In cruise mode, the high-tach Lycoming provides 75 percent power at 2670 rpm at 8500 feet for a speed of 131 mph TAS, providing a range of 529 miles plus 45-minute reserve.

Roomy cabin of Beech Sundowner.

Beech B-24R Sierra.

Beech B24R Sierra

In 1974 Beech Aircraft Corporation redesignated their Sierra 200 (for 200 hp) as Model B-24R due to installation of a new engine, the Lycoming I0-360-A1B6. The Sierra actually began in 1961 as a fixed-gear Musketeer, and in its B-24R form used a bigger, 76-inch diameter propeller for improved takeoff, climb, and cruise performance. It will true out at 160 mph, IAS at 10,000 feet full throttle and 2600 rpm, roughly 75 percent power.

The Sierra is generally similar to the Beech Sundowner but can carry from four to six people. Its electrically actuated hydraulic system uses a self-

contained unit in the rear fuselage, consisting of an electrically-driven hydraulic pump, fluid reservoir, and valves. An emergency valve, near the pilot's feet, allows selection of the landing gear to free-fall within three seconds. Main wheels retract outward into the wings, while the nosewheel turns through 90 degrees as it retracts rearward.

Standard equipment includes sensitive altimeter, fore and aft adjustable front seats with reclining backs, shoulder harness and lap belts, pilot's storm window, map stowage, ELT, stall warning horn, control locks, and towbar.

B-24R Sierra instrument panel.

Bell JetRanger III. (courtesy Bell Helicopter Textron)

Bell JetRanger III

The JetRanger III is the latest development of Bell's highly successful Model 206 series, which was originally developed in 1965 to meet the Army's need for a light observation helicopter. The evolution of the Jet-Ranger III has allowed the incorporation of the many safety, maintenance, and convenience features developed from the production and operational experience of over 6000 commercial and military JetRangers. Numerous optional accessories allow configuration conversion to meet the operational requirements of an executive transport, cargo carrier, aerial crane, ambulance, agricultural applications, and many more.

The five-place JetRanger III is powered by a 420-hp Allison 250-C20B turboshaft engine, which provides increased power and increased TBO for its modular components. The additional power means increased performance and greater productivity throughout the flight envelope, especially on hot days at high altitude. The engine is rated at 420 hp for takeoff and at 370 hp for maximum continuous power. At maximum internal gross weight (3200 lbs), the JetRanger III can hover in ground effect at 12,400 feet on a standard day.

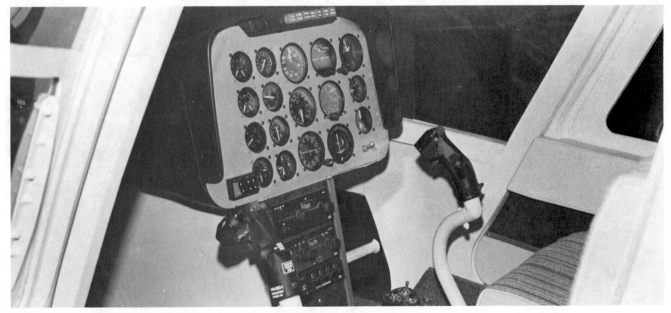

Bell JetRanger III cockpit. (courtesy Bell Helicopter Textron)

Bell 412. (courtesy Bell Helicopter Textron)

Bell 412

The Bell 412 is a powerful new 15-place helicopter with twin Pratt & Whitney PT6T-3B turbines and a new, advanced-design four-bladed rotor system. With cruise speed up to 130 knots and an offshore range of up to 350 nautical miles, the 412 is aimed at the petroleum industry, providing a fast, efficient crew change transport capability into the 1980s and beyond.

The 412 features an internal load capacity in excess of 5000 pounds and wide doors for easy loading; these make the helicopter ideal for rough terrain construction tasks and for supplying remote area job sites. For increased work handling versatility, the 412 has exceptional hot climate/high altitude operating characteristics. The 412 is also IFR certified for night flight and inclement weather conditions.

Bell 412 cockpit. (courtesy Bell Helicopter Textron)

Bellanca 14-19 Cruisemaster.

Bellanca 14-19 Cruisemaster

Bellanca's Model 14-19 Cruisemaster was produced between 1949-51 as a development of their earlier Model 14-13 Cruisair. The Model 14-19 carried the 190-hp Lycoming 0-435A, which gave it a cruise speed of 180 mph and a climb rate of 1400 fpm, with a range of 410 miles.

A later model, the 14-19-3, used the bigger 260-hp Continental engine that gave it a cruise speed of more than 200 mph. Roland Joslyn, of Malibu, California, bought a 1960 14-19-3 built by the Downer Aircraft Company, and completely reworked it. Joslyn's Cruisemaster, N6RJ, has a extended range of 750 miles and cruises at close to 200 mph with a 900-pound payload. He switched from trike gear to taildragger configuration, buried all antennas inside the glassed wings, and completely redid the interior, including a complete IFR panel.

Bellanca Cruisemaster panel.

Cessna C-34 Airmaster.

Cessna C-34 Airmaster

Cessna's four-seat cabin C-34 Airmaster monoplane first appeared in 1935 with 41 examples built. In an open competition at the National Air Races, the Cessna C-34 was officially proclaimed to be the "World's Most Efficient Airplane." Powered with a Warner Scarab seven-cylinder radial air-cooled engine of 145 horsepower with NACA cowling and pressure baffling, its panel was filled with Kollsman instruments that included altimeter, airspeed, compass, oil pressure and oil temperature gauges, plus electric starter and navigation lights.

The C-34 pictured here was re-engined by its owner, Clyde Bourgois, with a 165-horsepower Warner radial that provides similar performance to the original—V_{max} 158 mph, cruise 142 mph, climb 1000 fpm, ceiling 18,000 feet, stall 55 mph with flaps or 62 mph clean. Using an Aeromatic propeller for better climb, heavier wheels and a complete electrical system, his empty weight is 1500 pounds (120 lb more than the original) with the same gross weight of 2450 pounds.

Cockpit of C-34 Airmaster.

Cessna 140A.

Cessna 140A

Models 120 and 140 side-by-side two-seater Cessnas were manufactured from 1946 to 1948 and were virtually identical apart from such refinements in the 140 as starter, generator, battery, and manually operated flaps. In 1948, the improved Model 140A appeared with metal-skinned wings instead of fabric covering, and single wing struts in place of the former V-struts.

A fine example of the 140A is N1161D owned by Phil De Beixedon of Santa Barbara, California, which is powered with an 0-290-D2 Lycoming of 140 hp, far more than the original C85s and C90s when the 140A first appeared. Cruising at 75 percent power at 8500 feet altitude, De Beixedon's 140A trues out at 135 mph and burns 7.5 gph. Special 42-gallon Patroller tanks provide a range of 5 hours plus 45 minutes reserve.

Original 140As with 90 hp cruise around 110 mph with a 125-mph top speed and 40-mph stall.

Cessna 140A cockpit.

Cessna 150.

Cessna 150

Intended as a successor to Cessna's postwar 120/140 two-seaters, their 150 entered production in August, 1958, and nearly 3000 were built in the next six years, with close to 24,000 turned out in a 19-year production run. With a tricycle gear, the 150 appeared in three versions: the Standard, Trainer, and Commuter. In 1970 Cessna introduced the Model A150K Aerobat stressed to +6 and −3 Gs, permitting most normal aerobatic maneuvers such as snap rolls, barrel and aileron rolls, Cuban eights, loops, etc.

The Cessna 150 Commuter has a gross weight of 1600 pounds and an empty weight of 1111 pounds. With the 0-200 Continental engine of 100 hp, it cruises at 123 mph and climbs at 670 fpm to a ceiling of 14,000 feet. Range varies from 390 to 670 miles depending on fuel tankage. The Aerobat's optional equipment includes preselect flap control, vernier mixture control, and redesigned instrument panel for easier scanning.

Panel of Cessna 150.

Author's Cessna 170, N13DD.

Cessna 170

Cessna introduced their Model 170 in 1948 as virtually a four-seat version of the two-seater 120/140. It continued in production until 1956 when the Model 172 appeared with a tricycle landing gear. The initial production models, 170 and 170A, differed only in minor details.

I once owned an early Model 170 ragwing and found it a delight to fly into remote airstrips in Mexico, California, and Canada. Removing the back seat turned it into an excellent two-place flying camper with more than ample room for two backpacks, sleeping bags, tent, ice chest, and other gear for extended stays in the back country.

More than 5000 Cessna 170s were manufactured and today an estimated 3000 are still flying. Powered with the 145-hp Continental C145-2 engine, the 170 cruises at 121 mph and has a top speed of 143 mph. It climbs at 690 fpm to a service ceiling of 15,500 feet. Normal range is 590 miles.

Cockpit of Cessna 170 N13DD.

Cessna 172 Skyhawk.

Cessna 172 Skyhawk

For more than a decade Cessna's 172 Skyhawk has been the most popular four-place aircraft among General Aviation pilots. Introduced in 1956, the 172 was a revision of the 170 with a redesigned tail and tricycle landing gear. In 1960 the deluxe Skyhawk version came out with swept vertical fin, external baggage door, and shorter gear legs for easier entry.

In 1962 a wraparound rear window was added to provide a full 360-degree view. In 1977, the 145-hp Continental 0-300-C engine was replaced with the Lycoming 0-320-H of 160 hp. The 1970 models offered conical cambered wingtips, a light gray instrument panel and other small modifications. In 1971 a wider, softer spring-steel "Land-O-Matic" gear was added.

The Skyhawk 100, as the 1977 model was called, carries 43-54 gallons of fuel, has a top speed of 144 mph and a cruise of 140. Climb rate is 770 fpm, ceiling 14,200 feet, max range 726 miles.

Cessna Skyhawk panel.

Cessna 175 Skylark.

Cessna 175 Skylark

Introduced in 1960, Cessna's Model 175 Skylark is similar to the deluxe version of their Model 172 Skyhawk, but carries a more powerful engine with an electric pushbutton starter and vacuum pump drive. The Continental GO-300-E six-cylinder geared engine of 175 hp increased the cruise speed of the Skyhawk's 124 mph to 139 for the Skylark.

Other improvements included a free-blown windshield, electric fuel gauges, fiberglass speed fairings, and a redesigned instrument panel. The extra horsepower of the 175 upped the cruise speed 15 mph over the 172 and thus filled the gap between Cessna's 170 and 180 series aircraft.

Properly leaned out, the 175 cruises comfortably over a range of 560 miles burning 10.3 gph at 3050 engine rpm. For extended range flying, at 10,000 feet altitude, 2500 engine rpm gives a TAS of 106 mph, consumption of 7.2 gph, and a range of 770 miles.

Cessna 175 cockpit.

Cessna 180 (courtesy Cessna).

Cessna 180

In February 1953, Cessna began delivery of their Model 180, a four-place high-winger with the same wing as the 170 but an entirely redesigned fuselage, a new tail, and a more powerful engine. Models 180, 180A, and 180B were basically similar. In 1960 the 180C came out with more headroom for rear seat passengers. Model 180D followed with some equipment changes in 1961. In 1962 Model 180E featured a new fuel system, which extended range by 10 percent. In 1964 the Model 180G had an extra cabin window aft. The Model 180H in 1965 offered redesigned engine cowling doors and a different instrument panel. By 1977, a total of 5762 180s had been built.

Featuring a tailwheel-type landing gear and optional floatplane kit and ski axles, the 180 is a "go anywhere" aircraft. The Continental 0-470 engine delivers 230 hp for a normal cruise speed of 164 mph, ceiling of 19,600 feet and max range of 1215 miles.

Cessna 180 panel.

Cessna P337 Skymaster.

Cessna P337 Skymaster

Cessna's unique P-337 Skymaster is a tandem twin with a tractor engine up front and a pusher engine behind. Dual rudders are hung on twin booms that also support the horizontal elevator. Flying on one engine is simple, as there is no asymmetric thrust as in conventional twins.

The original Skymaster, the 336, used a fixed gear, with the retractable gear substituted in 1965 in the model 337. The Model P337 pressurized Skymas-ter is fitted with 225-horsepower turbocharged Continentals. The P337 seats five and has a top speed of 250 mph, cruising at 236 mph. Initial climb rate is 1250 fpm; range is 1133 miles; and ceiling is over 30,000 feet.

In the accompanying cockpit photo, pilot Ray Bailey of Gunnell Aviation in Santa Monica, California, demonstrates a "weightless" pushover maneuver that floats a cigarette package in the cockpit—a la space flight.

Pilot demonstrates "weightlessness" with cigarette package in pushover maneuver in P337 Skymaster.

D.H.82 Tiger Moth.

deHavilland D.H.82 Tiger Moth

One of the more graceful biplanes is the deHavilland D.H.82 Tiger Moth, which first flew October 26, 1931, as a derivation of the ultimate development of the D.H.60 Moth. It initially was called the D.H.60T Tiger Moth. The first D.H.82 was powered by a 120-hp Gipsy III engine. When the D.H.82A appeared in 1937, it received the more powerful Gipsy Major four-cylinder engine of 130 hp.

More than 1000 Tiger Moths were built prior to World War II and subsequently 4005 were built in the United Kingdom for the R.A.F as primary trainers. Another 1747 were built in Canada, mostly D.H.82Cs with enclosed cockpits for cold-weather flying; 1085 were built in Australia, and 345 in New Zealand. Performance included: 109 mph max speed; 90 mph cruise; 637 fpm initial climb; 13,600 feet ceiling; and 285 miles range. The example pictured here D.H.82A owned by movie actor Cliff Robertson, has a British naval liquid compass mounted in the front cockpit.

D.H.82 Tiger Moth panel.

Panel of P-51C Excalibur III. *(courtesy National Air and Space Museum, Smithsonian Institution)*

North American P-51C

Of more than 15,000 P-51 Mustangs of all types built by North American during World War II, none had a more distinguished career than P-51C-10 s/n 44-10947. Although '947 never saw combat, it was purchased as surplus by movie flier Paul Mantz and registered as NX 1202. Mantz flew the Mustang to victory in the 1946 and 1947 Bendix races, and the aircraft (flown by other pilots) took second and third places, respectively, in the 1948 and 1949 Bendix events. In 1947, Mantz also used NX 1202 to set two transcontinental speed records.

Mantz sold the Mustang to Charles Blair in 1950, in whose hands it would achieve further fame. Now named *Excalibur III*, NX 1202 made the first nonstop Fairbanks-Los Angeles flight and the first solo Fairbanks-New York flight. It set a transatlantic crossing record in 1951. Blair also flew *Excalibur III* from Norway to Fairbanks across the North Pole; aside from being the first solo flight of this kind, the flight pioneered polar navigation techniques.

NX 1202 was outfitted with upgraded avionics, including two automatic direction finders, two VHF transmitters and receivers, HF single-frequncy transmitter, master direction finder, and autopilot.

Cockpit of Excalibur III. *(courtesy National Air and Space Museum, Smithsonian Institution)*

Messerschmitt Bf. 109G-6/R3. (courtesy National Air and Space Museum, Smithsonian Institution)

Messerschmitt Bf. 109G-6/R3. (courtesy National Air and Space Museum, Smithsonian Institution)

Messerschmitt Bf. 109G

The state of the art in fighter aircraft design in the mid-1930s, Willy Messerschmitt's Bf. 109 was destined to remain in production and first-line service for a decade. Although it was outclassed by later Allied fighter types, a lack of foresight by the Nazi high command in selecting a follow-on design required that the 109 be constantly modified and updated throughout the war, even though it was obsolete. Nevertheless, the 109 was the preferred mount of the Luftwaffe's top aces, including all-time high-ranking Erich Hartmann (352 victories).

The Bf. 109 design did not die with the Third Reich. A Czech-built variant, the Avia CS.99, saw combat with the fledgling Israeli Air Force in 1948, and Spanish Rolls-Royce engined HA-1112 versions were in service until the 1960s.

The Bf. 109 was also the most-produced combat aircraft in history. The National Air and Space Museum's magnificently restored Bf. 109G-6/R3 is archetypical of the more than 30,000 built.

Messerschmitt Me 262A-1b. (courtesy National Air and Space Museum, Smithsonian Institution)

Messerschmitt Me 262

Messerschmitt's Me 262, the world's first operational jet fighter, was an amazing technological achievement but arrived too late in World War II to save a doomed Germany. Though 1,443 were built and as many as 300 saw combat, they constituted only a trickle against the tide of an Allied air force able to field 2000 bombers and 3000 fighters a day. Adolph Hitler is often blamed for delaying the production and deployment of the Me 262, but historical records would indicate that engine development problems were the principal cause for the fighter's late (autumn 1944) service introduction.

Nevertheless, the Me 262's Junkers Jumo 004 turbojet engines and swept wings clearly announced the dawn of a new era in aviation. Interestingly, the wings had been swept not for aerodynamic reasons, but to solve problems with the airplane's center of gravity.

The National Air and Space Museum's Me 262A-1b is believed to have flown with *Jagdgeschwader* 7, and differs from the basic A-1a fighter version only in that it carries wooden underwing "washboard" racks for air-to-air rockets.

Messerschmitt Me 262A-1b. (courtesy National Air and Space Museum, Smithsonian Institution)

Vought F4U-1D Corsair cockpit, left side. (courtesy National Air and Space Museum, Smithsonian Institution)

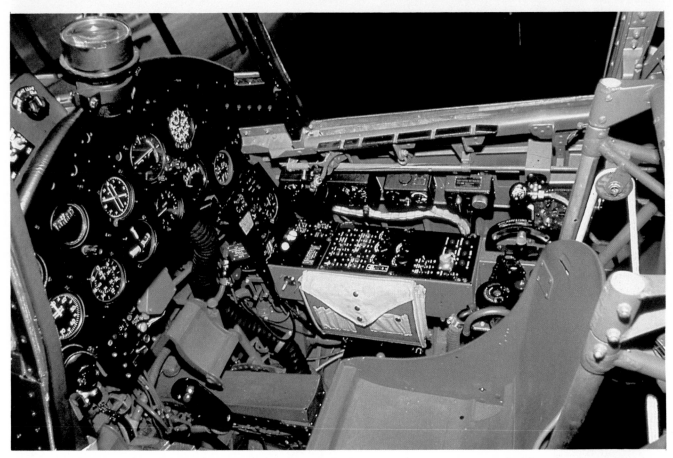

Vought F4U-1D Corsair cockpit, right side. (courtesy National Air and Space Museum, Smithsonian Institution)

Panel of Martin B-26 Flak Bait, a veteran of over 200 combat missions over Europe. The forward fuselage of this aircraft is on display at NASM. (courtesy National Air and Space Museum, Smithsonian Institution)

Pilot's area of B-26 Flak Bait. (courtesy National Air and Space Museum, Smithsonian Institution)

Cockpit of Lockheed XP-80 Shooting Star, prototype of America's first operational combat jet aircraft. (courtesy National Air and Space Museum, Smithsonian Institution)

Martin B-57 Canberra. (courtesy National Air and Space Museum, Smithsonian Institution)

Cessna T-37. (courtesy Cessna)

Boeing B-52H Stratofortress. (courtesy USAF)

Fairchild Republic F-105. (courtesy USAF)

Northrop F-5F front cockpit. (courtesy USAF)

Fairchild Republic A-10. (courtesy USAF)

McDonnell Douglas F-15 Eagle. (courtesy McDonnell Douglas)

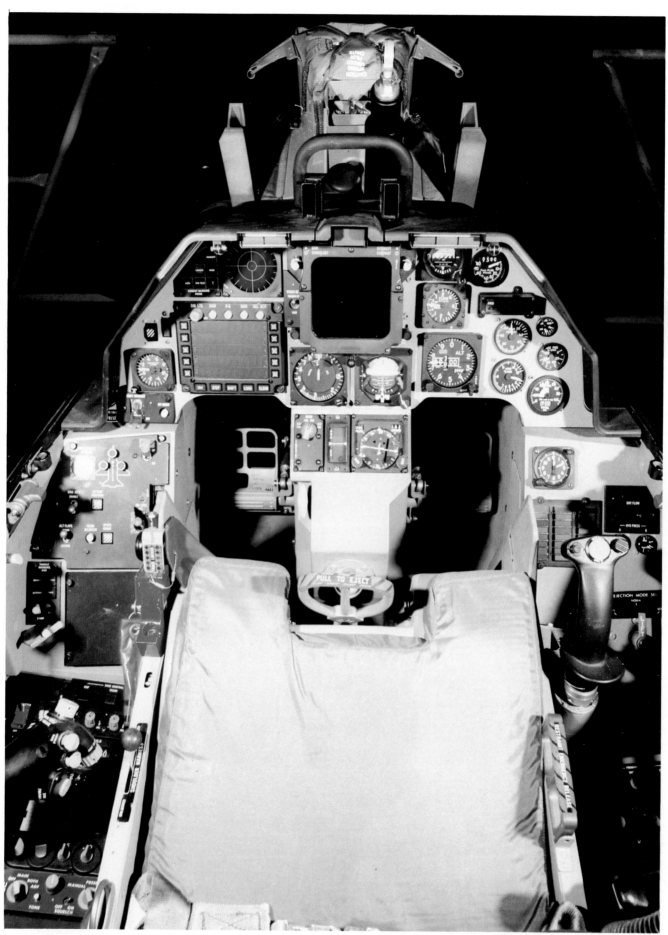

General Dynamics F-16B rear cockpit. (courtesy General Dynamics)

125

Lockheed L-1011 TriStar. (courtesy Lockheed)

Lockheed L-1011 TriStar cockpit mockup incorporating multi-color cathode ray tube (CRT) displays that provide pilots more accurate and reliable information on the status of all aircraft systems. These displays are expected eventually to replace most of the electromechanical instrumentation now in use.

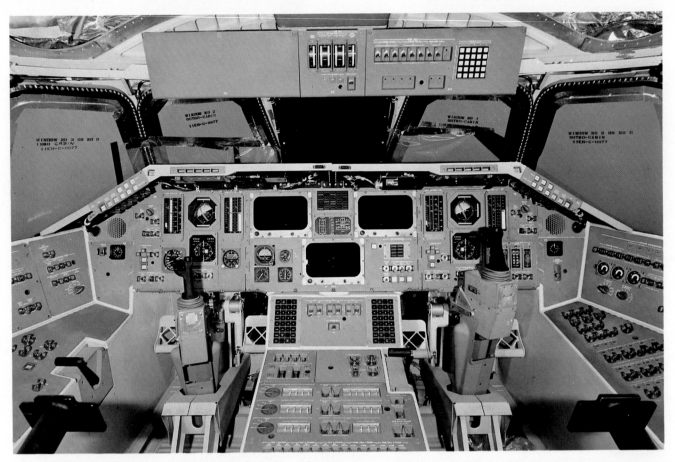

Space Shuttle Columbia. (courtesy Rockwell International)

Boeing 747. (courtesy Boeing)

Fairchild F-24W.

Fairchild F-24W

One of America's first executive transports was the Fairchild F-24R four-seat cabin monoplane that appeared in 1939, a follow-on to the three-seater F-24 that came out in 1933. The initial model was the F-24-R9; after U.S. entry in World War II, production of the F-24R continued for the USAAF as the UC-61K, with 306 being delivered. Production of the commercial model resumed in 1946 as the F-24R-46. The F-24R was powered with the 175-hp inverted Ranger

6-440-C2 engine that provided a speed of 133 mph max and a cruise of 118 mph.

The F-24W-41 version appeared in 1941 as the military UC-61. After the war, production resumed on the F-24W-46 model for civilian use. The Fairchild pictured here actually is a Model F-24W-46, built in 1946 by Temco. In 1948 it flew with the California Aeronautics Commission. In 1963 Chuck Gupton bought it and installed a zero-time 200-hp Ranger engine.

Cockpit of Fairchild F-24W.

Fleetwings Seabird.

Fleetwings Seabird

The Seabird amphibian was the first stainless steel aircraft ever certificated in the United States. The builder, Fleetwings, Inc., in 1934 had acquired Keystone Aircraft Corp. to build steel wings for the U.S. Army's Douglas Dolphin, and in 1936 the single-engine, four-place steel amphibian was launched into the Delaware River at Bristol, PA. Six aircraft were built, of which the prototype, SN1, is owned today by Channing Clark of Burbank, California.

The Seabird's 300-hp Jacobs engine gives it a cruise speed of more than 100 mph. The one owned by Mr. Clark is the sole survivor of the original six. Two were wrecked in Alaska; another crashed in a snowstorm; a fourth crashed in Michigan; and the fifth was sunk near Santa Catalina Island, California. Mr. Clark's Seabird flew coastal patrol for the Civil Air Patrol during World War II.

Cockpit of Fleetwings Seabird.

Grumman American AA-5B Tiger.

Grumman American AA-5B Tiger

Grumman American entered the highly competitive market for four-place, single-engine planes long dominated by the Big Three (Beech, Cessna and Piper), with their 1975 Model AA-5B Tiger. It was one of the series built by Grumman American that began with the AA-1 Yankee/Trainer, originally designed by James Bede and acquired by GA in 1964. The Trainer was a replacement for the first GA Yankee.

Next came the GA TR-2, an advanced trainer or deluxe version, which carried a cruise propeller for a higher top speed and greater range, followed by the four-place AA-5 Traveler, an enlarged version of the AA-1A Trainer, and then the Model AA-5B Tiger. It carries the 180-hp 0-360 Lycoming and can hit 170 mph, cruising at 160. Climb is 850 fpm; ceiling is 13,800 feet; and range is 752 miles. The cruise speed is some 15 to 20 mph faster than that of its competitors.

Cockpit of AA-5B Tiger.

Learjet 24D. *(courtesy Gates Learjet)*

Learjet 24D cockpit. *(courtesy Gates Learjet)*

Learjet 25 cockpit. *(courtesy Gates Learjet)*

Gates Learjet

Just as "Piper Cub" has entered the English language as a generic term for any light, privately owned aircraft, so the name "Learjet" has become synonomous with executive and corporate turbojet aviation. William P. Lear's dream of a six-passenger "mini-jet airliner"—a dream no other aircraft manufacturer believed in back in the late '50s and early '60s—became a reality in 1963 with the rollout and flight of the first Learjet 23, which embodied the objectives of optimum speed, comfort, utility, economy, and integrity.

Lear's dream has—quite literally—taken wing; the one-thousandth Learjet was delivered in March 1980, and the Learjet family of aircraft continues to grow. The Model 23 was upgraded to the Model 24 with birdproof windshield, engine fire protection, a new cabin pressurization system, and an additional 500 pounds allowable takeoff weight. The Model 25, stretched 52 inches to allow eight-passenger capability, was introduced in 1967. In 1973, two new models, the 35 and 36, were unveiled; featuring twin Garrett AiResearch TFE 731-2 turbofans, they were stretched an additional 13 inches and possessed unparalleled range/load and cost effectiveness.

Learjet 25. *(courtesy Gates Learjet)*

Learjet Longhorn 55. *(courtesy Gates Learjet)*

Learjet 35. (courtesy Gates Learjet)

Learjet 35/36 cockpit. (courtesy Gates Learjet)

The Longhorn series was introduced with the Models 28 and 29 in 1977. Their revolutionary wings employ advanced winglet technology and provide greatly enhanced fuel efficiency and performance.

Gates Learjet's largest aircraft to date, the 55 Longhorn series, first appeared in 1979. Featuring a roomier "stand-up" cabin, the Model 55 is certificated for flight up to 51,000 feet.

Learjet Longhorn 55 cockpit (courtesy Gates Learjet).

Howard DGA-11.

Howard DGA

First produced by Benny Howard in 1939, the DGA-15 was a commercial version of Benny's famous *Mr. Mulligan* racer of 1934 that won the Bendix Race in 1935. Designated DGA-6 (Benny's sixth *Damn Good Airplane*), *Mr. Mulligan* did not look like a racer—it carried four people as a high-wing cabin job with dual controls and a fat fuselage, powered with a Pratt & Whitney Wasp uprated to 830 hp. Benny won the Bendix by 23 seconds at 238.704 mph, barely nosing out Col. Roscoe Turner.

The DGA series of executive planes began with the DGA-8 (DGA-7 never flew). The DGA-8, 9, 11 and 12 were four-placers; DGA-15, 15P, and 15W carried five. Benny and his wife Maxine flew *Mr. Mulligan* in the 1936 Bendix Race but crashed in New Mexico when they lost a propeller blade. Bob Reichart, an airline pilot, recovered the wreckage, rebuilt it, and in October, 1977, tried for a world speed record in its class at Mud Lake, Nevada. Again the DGA-6 crashed. Reichart and his wife were both killed.

Panel of DGA-11.

Hughes 500D. (courtesy Hughes Helicopters)

Hughes 500D

The Hughes 500 series of helicopters is the commercial derivative of the OH-6 Cayause developed for the Army as a light observation helicopter in the 1960s. Also known as the "Loach," the OH-6 equipped scout platoons of Air Cavalry units and saw service in Vietnam. An improved version, the OH-6A, incorporated an engine exhaust muffler, five-blade main rotor, and reshaped rotor tips, which justified its nickname of "The Quiet One."

"The Quiet One" modifications are also carried by the civilian Model 500D which is powered by a 420-hp Allison 250-C20B turbojet. Its distinctive T-tail improves handling in abnormal maneuvers and increases stability in both high and low speed flight. Normally configured for pilot and four passengers, the 500D can accommodate up to six passengers or two litters and two medical attendants.

Hughes 500D panel. (courtesy Hughes Helicopters)

Lake LA-4-200 Buccaneer.

Lake LA-4-200 Buccaneer

The four-place Lake LA-4-200 Buccaneer amphibian is a development of the original Colonial C-2 Skimmer IV, a design created by a group of Grumman engineers that included Dave Thurston and Herb Lindblad. Thurston left the group to market his two-place Teal with Schweizer Aircraft, and Linblad joined Aerofab in Sanford, Maine, who builds the Buccaneer.

Powered with the Lycoming I0-360-A1B of 200 hp, the Buccaneer uses the NACA 4415 airfoil of the C-2 Skimmer, which permits good control during slow flight, the LA-4-200 Buccaneer, which received certification in 1970, has all-metal ailerons and hydraulically operated, slotted flaps along 80 percent of its wingspan.

The Buccaneer cruises at 150 mph, has a ceiling of 14,700 feet, and an 825-mile range. It gets off the water in 1100 feet or 600 feet on land and splashes down in 600 feet.

Lake LA-4-200 cockpit.

Luscombe 8E Silvaire.

Luscombe 8E Silvaire

Don Luscombe's two-place Model 8 Silvaire first appeared in 1937, with deliveries commencing the following year as the Luscombe "Fifty" (50-horsepower Continental A50). Next came the Model 8A Luscombe "Sixty Five" (65-hp Continental A65). Model 8B used the 65-hp Lycoming. Models 8C and 8D had the 75-hp Continental A75.

A total of 1200 Luscombe Silvaires were built from 1938 to 1942 when Luscombe Airplane concentrated on war work. Production of the Silvaire was resumed in 1946 with Models 8E and 8F, essentially similar, with 85- and 90-hp Continental engines respectively. In 1949 Temco built 50 Silvaires, and in 1955 Silvaire Aircraft Company was formed, Model 8Fs were built until 1960. With the 90-hp engine the Silvaire could cruise at 120 mph, climb at 900 fpm, and had a range of 500 miles.

Cockpit of Luscombe 8E.

Maule Strata-Rocket.

Maule Strata-Rocket

A growing favorite bush plane is the Maule Strata-Rocket 4-place, high-wing taildragger. Powered with a 220-hp Franklin 6A-350, it has true STOL performance, being able to get off the ground in 400 feet and land in 390 feet. Climb rate is 1250 fpm, ceiling 19,000 feet, making it an excellent performer for mountain flying.

With an empty weight of 1250 pounds and 2300-pound gross weight, its wing loading is 14 lb/sq ft., and power loading is 10.4 lb/hp. Top speed is 188 mph; cruising speed is 180 mph at 75 percent power, and range is 680 miles. The Strata-Rocket stalls at 40 mph.

Introduced in 1967, the Maule Strata-Rocket was one of a series powered with engines from 145 to 235 hp. The fuselage is fiberglass-covered steel tubing; the wings are all metal, with two-position flaps.

Cockpit of Maule Strata-Rocket.

Mooney Executive M20F.

Mooney Executive M20F

The 1975 Mooney four-place Executive M20F is a stretched version of the Mooney Ranger, with a bigger, 200-hp Lycoming I0-360-A1B6D powerplant and a stretched fuselage that provides more leg room and a bigger baggage area, plus additional cabin windows. The engine drives a constant-speed Hartzell two-bladed metal propeller. The engine has fuel injection, tuned induction manifold, exhaust-temperature gauge, and ram-air power boost. With a max speed at sea level of 177 mph, it stalls at 62 mph IAS dirty. Climb is better than 1000 fpm, service ceiling 16,000 feet, range 989 miles.

The cockpit panel is topped with a glare shield; below that fuel gauges calibrated in pounds, plus oil temperature/pressure gauges. Flight instruments are at left, NAV/COMM at center. At center below the panel is the power console with throttle, pitch and mixture controls, flap control, and parking brake.

Cockpit of Mooney Executive.

Noorduyn Norseman.

Noorduyn Norseman

Specifically designed for Canadian bush flying, the Norseman light freighter and 8-10-seat transport first flew in 1935 powered with a Canadian Wright R-975-E3 radial of 450 hp. The production version of this model was known as the Norseman II, followed in 1937 by the Norseman IV which used the 600-hp Pratt & Whitney R-1340-S3H1 Wasp engine. The Norseman IV was ordered by the R.C.A.F. for radio and navigation training, and after trials with seven similar craft designated YC-64, it was adopted in 1942 by the USAF, with 746 Norsemen delivered to USAF as C-64As. In 1946 the Canadian Car & Foundry Company took over the Noorduyn assets and developed an improved model, the Mk V, produced until 1950.

The Norseman, powered with either the 600-hp Pratt & Whitney S3H1 or R-1340-AN-1 Wasp, has a V_{max} of 155 mph, cruises at 141 mph at 66 percent power at 5000 feet, has a service ceiling of 17,000 feet and a range of 464 miles.

Cockpit of Noorduyn Norseman.

Partenavia P-68.

Partenavia P-68

Partenavia Construczioni Aeronautiche was founded in Naples, Italy, in 1957 by Professor Ing Luigi Pascale, who designed a series of light aircraft. Two popular models were the P-68B Victor twin-engined seven-seat aircraft and its derivatives, and the P-66C Charlie. Developed from the basic P-68, the P-68B Victor has been in production at Naples since 1974.

A recent derivative of the P-68B Victor is the P-68C Charlie powered with two Lycoming I0-360-A1B engines of 200 hp each, along with all other parts made in America and shipped to Italy for assembly. The P-68C has a V_{max} of 200 mph, cruises at 191 mph at 75 percent power or 185 at 65 percent power. The gear is fixed tricycle type, and two integral fuel tanks in the wing each hold 71 U.S. gallons. The high-wing configuration permits the air intakes and propeller tips to clear ground debris for better engine life. Mira Slovak Aviation at Santa Paula Airport, California, is the U.S. distributor.

Partenavia P-68 cockpit.

Patchen Explorer.

Patchen Explorer

The Patchen Explorer was a development of the former Thurston Aircraft Corporation as a landplane version of its TSC-1 Teal amphibian, financed by Marvin Patchen Inc., which retained rights to the TSC-2 Explorer. A variant, the Observer, was to have been produced for law enforcement with the advantage of exceptional cockpit visibility.

The prototype Explorer completed its flight test program in November, 1972, after which a market survey was conducted to determine special requirements of pipeline patrol operators, aerial photographers, and law enforcement agencies. Patchen sold the rights to the Explorer in May, 1975, to Dr. Maitland Reed in South Africa, where it underwent certification tests.

A four-seater, it used the Lycoming I0-360-A1A 200-horsepower engine, cruised at 128 mph, and came equipped with searchlight, siren, PA system, and camera mounts.

Cockpit of Patchen Explorer.

Piper J-3 Cub.

Piper J-3 Cub

The airplane that made the name *Cub* a household word was born in 1937 as a development of the earlier J-2 of 1936. Initially it was powered with a Continental A-40-4 engine of 40 hp and later with 50-hp Continentals, Franklins, or Lycomings. A stripped version of the 40-hp Cub was the Cub Trainer, and in 1939 the J-3 Cub made way for its successor, the J-4 Cub Coupe.

More than 5500 of the tandem, two-seat, fabric-covered planes were produced before production was suspended temporarily in 1942; production resumed in 1945 with a bigger engine, the 65-hp Continental A65. In 1947 several revisions changed the nomenclature to the PA-11 Cub Special. Today more than 3600 Cubs and more than 500 Cub Specials remain currently active in America. The 65-hp Cub has a top speed of 100 mph and cruises at 87 mph on 75 percent power. Initial climb is 514 fpm; service ceiling is 14,500 feet; and range is 300 miles.

Cockpit of J-3 Cub.

143

Piper PA-22-150 Tri-Pacer.

Piper PA-22-150 Tri-Pacer

Piper's PA-22 Tri-Pacer was born in 1951 as a redesigned PA-20 Pacer. As the conventional-geared Pacer showed a tendency to swerve on landings in a stiff crosswind, Piper designed a tricycle version of the same aircraft that came to be called the "Flying Milkstool." Originally powered with a 125-hp engine, the engine was uprated every two years—in 1953 to 135 hp; to 150 hp in 1955 and 160 hp in '57.

The 150-hp model was called the Caribbean in 1959-60. The four-seat arrangement, although crowded in the rear, proved popular.

With a top speed of 141 mph and a cruise of 134 mph, the 160-hp version nevertheless had excellent takeoff and climb performance compared with its competitors and can nose out the Cessna 172 on cross-country runs.

Cockpit of Piper Tri-Pacer.

Piper Cherokee Six PA 32-300.

Piper Cherokee Six

The Cherokee Six, with fixed gear, can carry six people at 180 mph behind a 300-hp Lycoming, thus offering light twin performance with single-engine economy. Introduced in 1965 as a six-seater, in 1966 it was approved for an optional seventh seat. In 1969 the Cherokee Six B had more cabin space by moving the instrument panel further forward.

The 300-hp version came out in 1970 and is convertible to a cargo hauler by easy seat removal. In 1978, increased speed capability made the Sixes the fastest planes in their class. A 5 percent increase in range was achieved with aerodynamic cleanup. In 1979 a 98-gallon fuel tankage gave the Six a range of 923 miles at 65 percent power.

V_{max} of the 300-hp Cherokee Six is 174 mph, or 168 mph at 75 percent power in cruise. Max range at 55 percent power is 857 miles; ceiling is 16,250 feet, and ROC is 1050 fpm.

Cockpit of Cherokee Six.

Piper Lance.

Piper Lance

The Piper Cherokee Lance is basically a Cherokee Six with retractable landing gear, the same gear as in the Seneca with the Arrow's retraction system. A useful load of 1690 pounds allows for six passengers with luggage and full fuel. The engine is the fuel-injected IO-540-KIG5 engine of 300 hp. Designated PA-32R-300, it first flew in 1974.

The 1977 version came with complete electronics grouping as in the Cherokee Cruiser's custom package, including Piper TruSpeed indicator, I-panel white backlighting with overhead red spotlight, cabin dome, navigation, landing/taxi and radio dimming lights, rotating beacon, 3-inch pictorial gyro horizon, 3-inch directional gyro, pictorial turn rate indicator, OAT gauge, ROC indicator, electric clock, and engine-driven vacuum pump. She'll do 190 mph level, cruise at 182 mph at 75 percent power, climb at 1000 fpm to 14,600 feet, and fly 995 miles nonstop at 55 percent power.

Piper Lance cockpit.

Piper Apache PA-23.

Piper Apache

Of all the Piper Indian braves, their Apache is hailed as the first successful light twin. It dates back to 1952 when a model called the Twin-Stinson appeared, the first Piper of Stinson lineage since the Piper Stinson Flying Station Wagon, powered with a pair of 125-hp Lycoming engines.

First announced in September of 1962, the PA-23-235 Apache introduced a number of design re-finements that markedly changed its appearance. Basically a four-seater with an optional fifth seat, it was powered with two 235-hp Lycoming 0-540-B1A5 engines. Certain features of the Piper Aztec were introduced, including the swept vertical tail fin and all-moving horizontal surfaces. The Apache was popular as a twin-engined trainer, and a number have been further modified with bigger engines and other goodies.

Cockpit of Piper Apache.

Piper PA-23-250 Aztec C.

Piper PA-23-250 Aztec C

The PA-23-250 cabin twin was introduced in 1962 as the six-seat Aztec B, an improved version of the original five-seat Aztec A, which in turn was very similar to the PA-23-235 Apache, which it preceded. The Aztec B differed in having a long nose, a modified instrument panel, and improved maintenance accessibility. In 1960 the United States Navy bought 20 Aztec A aircraft off the shelf as U-11As. Others went to the Peruvian Navy and Argentine Army.

Evolved from the earlier Apache, the Aztec adopted many of its proven systems and components. In 1964 the Aztec C was introduced and featured redesigned engine nacelles, a modified landing gear, and I0-540-C4B5 engines of 250 hp each. The Aztec C's V_{max} is 218 mph, 75 percent cruise 208 mph, climb 1490 fpm, ceiling 19,800 feet, range 1320 miles.

Cockpit of Piper Aztec.

Ryan PT-22.

Ryan PT-22

In 1934 the Ryan ST series of tandem two-seat primary trainers went into production. One of the first off the line was purchased by the U.S. Army Air Corps for evaluation as the XPT-16. Another fifteen aircraft, like the prototype powered with the 125-hp Menasco L-365-1 engine, were delivered in 1939 as YPT-16s. In 1940 another forty were ordered as PT-16s.

In the following year, Menasco engines were discarded by the USAAC in favor of the Kinner R-440 radial. The resulting model was the ST-3KR, ordered in 1941 as the PT-21. One hundred PT-21s were fol-lowed by 1023 PT-22s for Civilian Pilot Training Program schools, which were powered with the Kinner R-540-1 engines. Twenty-five were taken over by the AAC from Dutch contracts to become PT-22As, and 250 PT-22s were re-engined after delivery with the R-540-3s to become PT-22Cs. Production ended in 1942. With the 160-hp Kinner radial, the Ryan ST-3KR had a V_{max} of 131 mph, cruised at 123 mph, and climbed at 100 fpm, with a 352-mile range. The PT-22 shown here is owned by Bob Yates of San Jose, California, who re-engined it with a Ranger engine and added cowl flaps.

Ryan PT-22 cockpit.

Ryan Navion Model D.

Ryan Navion Model D

Originally designed by North American Aviation, who produced some 1000 aircraft of this type, the Navion was built during 1948-50 by the Ryan Aeronautical Company, who built another 1000 machines. In 1951, Ryan introduced a new, more powerful model, the Navion Super 260 with the Lycoming G0-435-C2 engine of 260 hp. In 1961 production began on a still newer version by Navion Aircraft Company, the Navion Rangemaster G-1.

The Model D Navion shown here, owned by Jim Snow of Los Angeles, has the bigger G0-435-C2 engine and cruises at 165 mph IAS at altitude on full throttle and 2600 rpm. V_{max} is 170. Ruggedly built, the Navion has retractable gear and some, like Snow's, carries the "Palo Alto" tail, with the stabilizer leading edge raised 2 or 3 degrees so the wing flies as a lower angle of attack. The result is a speed increase of 10 mph.

Model D Navion cockpit.

Stinson 108-3 Voyager.

Stinson 108 Voyager

Stinson's Model 108 Voyager was a scaled-up postwar development of their 1940 three place Model 10, itself an improved version of the earlier Model 105 Voyager introduced in 1939. A four-seater, the Model 108 first appeared in 1946 with a 150-hp Franklin 6A4-150-B31 powerplant. The Model 108-1 came out with minor improvements, and a switch to the 165-hp Franklin 6A4-165-B3 resulted in Model 108-2. At the same time a similarly-powered utility version was introduced as the Stinson Station Wagon.

Late in 1948 the final version of the Voyager, Model 108-3, was introduced with an increased vertical fin area and a bigger fuel tank. Piper Aircraft then took over production until 1950 and assembled a few more Voyagers before shutting down the line. The Model 108-3 Voyager had a V_{max} of 146 mph, cruised at 130 mph, climbed at 770 fpm, and had a 14,000-foot ceiling and a 554-mile range.

Cockpit of Stinson 108-3.

Temco TE-1B Buckaroo.

Temco TE-1B Buckaroo

The Buckaroo tandem two-seat trainer appeared in 1949 as an adaptation of the Globe Swift. It utilized some 80 percent of the earlier cabin monoplane's tooling. Seventeen examples of the Buckaroo were built: two prototypes, three service test aircraft for the USAF designated the YT-35, ten delivered to Saudi Arabia, and one each to Italy and Israel.

The three YT-35s were eventually declared surplus. The prototypes were powered with 145-hp

Continental C145-2Hs as TE-1As. The TE-1B was built for USAF evaluation with the 165-hp Franklin 6A4-165-B3.

The sole surviving TE-1B Buckaroo is owned by John O'Crowley of Van Nuys, California, who completely restored it with a 210-hp Continental engine, which gives a cruise of 162 mph at 65 percent power. With the original 165-hp Franklin, the Buckaroo had a V_{max} of 156 mph, 1000 fpm climb, and 17,000-foot ceiling.

Cockpit of Temco Buckaroo.

Varga Kachina.

Varga 2150A Kachina

The Varga Kachina two-place tandem sport plane originated in 1957 as the Morrisey Nifty Model 1000C, conceived and built by Bill Morrisey, a former Douglas test pilot who won an Approved Type Certificate for it. It was Morrisey's idea that the thousands of returning GI pilots would enjoy flying a sport plane that looked and felt like a WWII trainer.

When his dream fell through, Morrisey sold production rights for the Nifty to Clifford Shinn. Shinn built some 35 Model 2150As before he turned over the business to George Varga, of Chandler, Arizona. Chandler set up a family production line for the Model 2150A Kachina, named for the Hopi Indian doll. Where Morrisey's original version was built of plywood, the Kachina is all metal, and carries a 150-hp Lycoming 00320-A2C engine. It has a V_{max} of 148 mph, cruises at 135 mph, climbs 1450 fpm, and has a 525-mile range.

Cockpit of Varga Kachina.

Chapter 9
The
Military Way

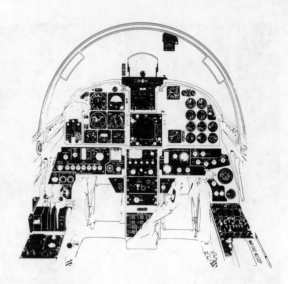

The airplane was barely a decade old when the greatest fears of early thinkers, on the destructive potential of a war in the air, exploded over Europe, in World War I. First came flimsy observation planes that served as artillery spotters. Then defensive fighter planes were hurriedly launched to meet the deadly threat of the German Zeppelin raids over England. Finally, there were multi-engined bombers, escorted by agile open cockpit biplanes, whose pilots flew to glory on both sides in personal one-to-one combat duels.

Needless to say, the cockpits of these early fighters and bombers were crude, unheated, exposed to the elements, and equipped with only rudimentary flight and engine gauges—magnetic compasses instead of modern gyros; airspeed indicators, altimeters, tachometers, and not much else.

Over the years, sophistication of military aircraft cockpit design has grown with the current state of the art. Thanks to General Jimmy Doolittle, "blind flight" has become commonplace. Various gyro instruments and avionics equipment have replaced the earth's horizon for reference at night or in weather.

Visual coding found its place in cockpit design, to speed recognition and interpretation of "extra-sensory perception" flying—by instruments, rather than reception solely by eye and ear (and kinesthetics). For example, when driving along a highway, we use visual codes to warn us of danger or give us other information. Spots of color, numbers, letters, lines, arrows, lights are all symbolic codes that must be learned. Once mastered, they become effective means of supplying information quickly, while poorly designed codes cause confusion and lead to accidents.

Today's high-speed aircraft require maximum efficiency in instrument readout by pilots who may be flying at Mach 3 and at stratospheric altitudes. To meet this challenge for emerging aircraft of the 1980s, consider the Collins Electronic Flight Instrument System (EFIS), which represents the state of the art in electronic displays.

These instruments offer new capability and flexibility for the world's most advanced cockpits and many advantages over older mechanical displays. An ability to present information with better comprehension is of primary importance. Typically, the new Collins cathode ray tube (CRT) displays use multi-color shadow mask technology.

Shadow mask CRT displays offer bright, full-spectrum colors. Primary colors are red, blue, and green. Several derivative colors include white, which is easily synthesized. Integral contrast enhancement filters used with the high-resolution shadow mask tubes make these displays exceptionally readable, even under full-sunlight cockpit-lighting conditions.

The basic shadow mask CRT tube consists of a three-gun assembly, shadow mask, faceplate with phosphor coating, and a glass envelope to encase the elements. A delta electronic gun assembly provides improved convergence and mechanical rigidity, and the high-resolution shadow mask provides four to six times better resolution than does your home TV set.

Many such revolutionary cockpit displays are, of course, a spinoff from the Space Age technology that equipped the Apollo and Shuttle spacecraft with ultra-modern CRTs and advanced mechanical instruments that take much of the workload off the aircrews.

On the following pages, you will be able to trace the development of today's super-sophisticated military cockpits from early conceptualities, when pilots relied more on their own sensory perceptions of altitude, airspeed, attitude, etc., than on cockpit displays that virtually think for the pilots.

Beech T-34C. (courtesy Beech)

T-34C front panel. (courtesy Beech)

T-34C rear panel. (courtesy Beech)

Beech T-34C

Designed as a military primary flight trainer for the jet age, the first Beech T-34 Mentor flew in 1948 and was based largely on the V-35 Bonanza airframe. Accepted by the services in 1953, 353 T-34As were produced for the Air Force while the Navy took delivery of 423 T-34Bs. Although both versions were powered by the Continental E-225 0-470-13 engine of 225 hp, the Navy's Bs featured a strengthened landing gear structure to take the punishment of carrier landing training.

Beech undertook development of the turbine-engined T-34C in the early '70s, and the Navy received its first "Charlies" in 1976. The T-34C's derated PT-6 turboprop engine produces 400 hp, nearly twice as much as the recip engine, and results in jetlike handling for fledgling Naval aviators. A new version, the T-34C-1, is being prepared for export sales as a weapons-delivery trainer and features a PT-6 turboprop of 550 hp.

A number of T-34A and B models are owned and operated by individuals, flying clubs, and Civil Air Patrol units, and the Mentors are gaining acceptance as "real warbirds" on the airshow and fly-in scenes. Perhaps the most striking difference between the T-34 and its Bonanza progenitor is in the cockpit, which employs tandem seating and military-type controls and instruments. Compare these photos with those of the V-35 Bonanza cockpit on page 98.

Bell AH-1S Cobra. (courtesy Bell Helicopter Textron)

Bell AH-1S Cobra

Design work in the '50s and experience with the 1961 Warrior mockup and the 1962-64 Sioux Scout prototype led to the construction of the first HueyCobra in 1965. By August 1967, the AH-1G was in service in Vietnam. Production of the Army's first special purpose helicopter continued until 1973. During that five year period, 1126 AH-1Gs were produced at the rate of 35 per month. In Vietnam, the AH-1G established an enviable record in over one million combat flight hours.

Today's AH-1S is not the Cobra of 1967. Evolving from a successful lineage of Bell attack helicopters, the new AH-1S is another step in updating a proven system to meet the changing nature of the battlefield. The sophisticated cockpit of the AH-1S features head-up display, multi-function horizontal and vertical situation indicator, low airspeed data sensor display, radar altimeter, radar warning display, laser tracker control, TOW missile control panel, and Doppler navigation control; the instruments are compatible with night vision goggles, which permit "blackout flight" at night.

AH-1S gunner's panel. (courtesy Bell Helicopter Textron)

AH-1S pilot's panel. (courtesy Bell Helicopter Textron)

Boeing P-26A fighter of U.S. Army.

Boeing P-26A

In January, 1933, the United States Army ordered 111 P-26As (Model 266) from Boeing, a radical departure from the earlier Boeing P-12F biplane fighter in that it had a single, low wing with outside bracing wires. The Model 266 followed an earlier monoplane design, the Model 248, which was built by Boeing in 1932 as a private venture. The pilot sat high above the 550-hp R-1340-21 radical engine. Flying wires connected the wings to wheel pants while landing wires tied the wings to the top of the metal fuselage.

The Army P-26As looked quite similar but carried the 600 hp Pratt & Whitney R-1340-27 radial en-gine with the new NACA cowling. Wing flaps also were used. Some of these Boeing fighters saw action against Japan in August 1937 in China, and in De-cember 1941 in the Philippines.

Cockpit instrumentation was rudimentary. The top panel included airspeed, magnetic compass, tachometer and clock, left to right. Below were altime-ter, turn and bank, oil pressure/temperature, and manifold pressure. Left of the panel were the starter handle, magneto switches, master switch, and amme-ter. Fuel switches and gauges were mounted below the instrument panel, and throttle quadrant was at the pilot's left.

Boeing P-26A fighter cockpit of 1934.

Boeing B-17G Flying Fortress.

Boeing B-17 Flying Fortress

As far back as 1933, the U.S. Air Corps dreamed of a huge bomber that could carry a ton of explosives 5000 miles, under a secret memo called "Project A." This RFP led to Boeing's remarkable XB-15 research plane that could fly 5130 miles at 152 mph. This gave Boeing the idea to design a new long-range bomber, Model 299, using four engines like the XB-15, to protect the American coastline from foreign surface fleets. This role suggested its name—the "Flying Fortress."

Rushed to completion in one year, the 299 was flown from Seattle to Wright Field nonstop a month after rollout at an unheard of 252 mph. Sadly, it crashed when the test pilot took off with the controls inadvertently locked. However, the Army ordered a baker's dozen production versions, the YB-17s, and later supercharged versions for high-altitude bombing missions.

First into large scale production was the B-17F, of which 3400 were built, and then came the B-17G, with a molded plastic nose and a double-barreled gun turret beneath it for defense against frontal attack. Some 6430 were built to fight the air war over Fortress Europe in World War II. The last B-17 in U.S. Service, a QB-17 drone, ironically was shot down in 1960 by a Boeing Bomarc missile.

Boeing B-17G cockpit.

Boeing B-50 Superfortress.

Boeing B-50 Superfortress

The Boeing B-50 Superfortress dates back to the post-World War II period of the "Cold War" between the United States and Russia, when the Strategic Air Command needed a replacement for the B-29 to deter Soviet aggression with the threat of long-range nuclear bombing. In May, 1945, a prototype, the XB-44, was flown by Boeing, consisting of a B-29A fitted with P&W R-4360 Wasp Major engines.

The production bombers were relabeled the B-50 and first flew on June 25, 1947, armed with 13 .50-caliber machine guns and with a tail so tall it had to be folded to get into a hangar. In February, a B-50A flew around the world nonstop, using in-flight refueling, while a competitive long-range bomber, the Northrop YB-49 "Flying Wing" was regarded as too unstable in pitch to serve as a bombing platform. A total of 80 B-50As were built, plus 50 B-50Bs.

Boeing built 122 B-50Ds with built-in provision for flying boom aerial refueling and 700-gallon drop tanks under each wing. Rendered tactically obsolete with advent of newer jet bombers, most B-50s were converted to flying gas stations for the Tactical Air Command between 1957 and 1959. Single jet pods were installed under each wing to increase maximum formatting speed and altitude capabilities.

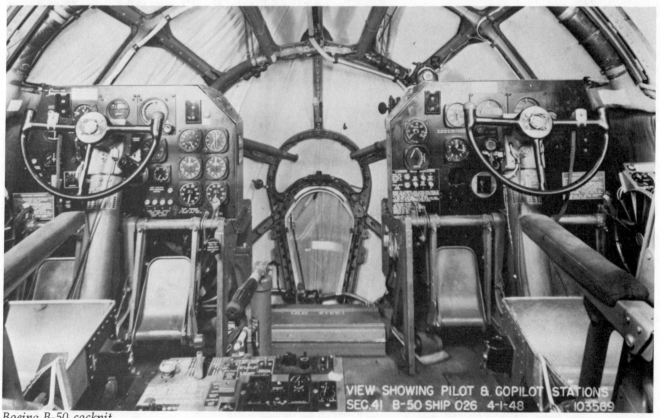

Boeing B-50 cockpit.

Boeing B-47 Strato Jet. (courtesy Boeing)

Boeing B-47 Stratojet

First flight of the Boeing XB-47 took place on December 17, 1947, based on the design of Boeing's Model 450, which incorporated a wing sweepback of 35 degrees after a study of captured German documents suggested its advantage in high-speed flight. By 1948 the USAF had ordered the B-47 into production, while cautiously reserving its primary funds for the obsolescent B-36.

The Korean War stimulated the largest bomber production program since World War II, and Boeing-Wichita was joined by reopened factories of Douglas at Tulsa and Lockheed at Marietta in turning out B-47s. Principal Stratojet model was the B-47E,

which could carry a nuclear bomb. When B-47 Stratojet production ended in February, 1957, 28 Strategic Air Command medium bomber and five reconnaissance wings used them.

By that time, the majority of B-47s in bomber configuration were modified, mainly by strengthening the wings for low-level "LOB" bombing missions—in LOB bombing the aircraft streaks toward the target at V_{max} and treetop height, releases its bomb during a vertical zoom, and escapes destruction by completing a half-loop and half-roll, called an Immelman turn. Pilots called this model a "six-engined fighter."

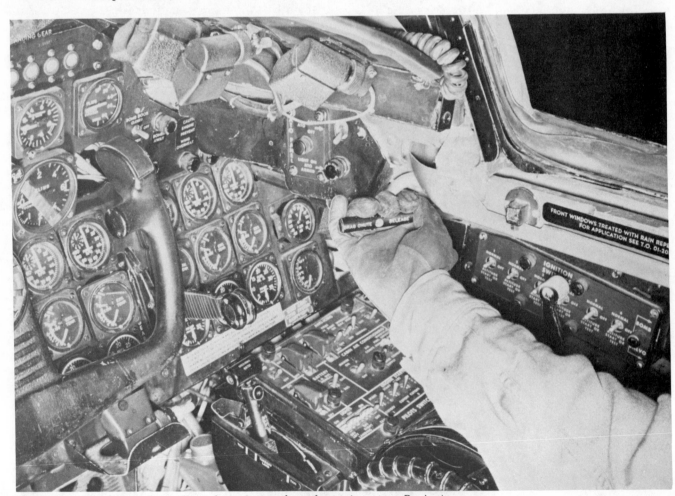

Boeing B-47 cockpit, pilot pulling drag-chute release lever. (courtesy Boeing)

Boeing B-52 Superfortress.
(courtesy Boeing)

Boeing B-52 Stratofortress

History of the Boeing B-52 Superfortress dates back to 1946 when the USAF issued an RFP for an intercontinental bomber. Boeing's first proposal was a straight-wing design carrying six 5500-hp Wright T-35 turboprops, weighing 180 tons. In 1948, Pratt & Whitney's XJ-57 engine looked better, and the design was frozen to include eight J-57s suspended on pods below a wing swept back 35 degrees.

The first XB-52 flew October 2, 1952, with eight J57-P-3s slung under 36.5-degree swept wings. Pilot and copilot sat under a narrow canopy. Eight main wheels retracted into the fuselage and small outrigger wheels were at the wingtips. The K-1A bombing system was located in the nose.

USAF Secretary Donald A. Quarles called the B-52 "The most formidable expression of air power in the history of military aviation . . . able to find and hit any target anywhere in the world in any weather." The B-52 was mated to the awesome hydrogen bomb, the first of which a B-52 dropped at Eniwetok November 2, 1952.

The B-52 cockpit includes the most sophisticated navigation equipment available, including the electro-video system (EVS) control panel shown in the photo of the cockpit of a B-52 of the 28th Bomb Wing. A total of 744 Stratofortresses were built, and it is likely that the B-52 will remain in service into the 21st century.

Cockpit of B-52H Superfortress. (courtesy USAF)

Boeing E-4 Command Post.

Boeing E-4 Command Post

In the event of an all-out nuclear holocaust, the Strategic Air Command has prepared to direct the doomsday war from the stratosphere—not in space-craft, but aboard a modified Boeing 747B Advanced Airborne Command Post, or AABNCP, known to the USAF as E-4. Three E-4As now in service are able to operate as National Emergency Airborne Command Posts (NEACPS) until later models, the E-4Bs, are operational.

The E-4 is designed for long-endurance missions. Its 4620 square feet of floor space accommodate six areas on the main deck: the National Command Authorities' (NCA) work area, conference room, briefing room, battle staff work area, communications control center, and rest area. The flight deck accommodates the flight crew, navigation station, and flight crew rest area. Lobe areas under the main deck house a technical control facility and limited on-board maintenance storage area.

The first E-4B flew in the spring of 1976 with a new 1200kVA electrical system to operate the advanced electronics gear to come later. Interestingly, the radio gear will include a new IF/VLF system employing a trailing wire antenna, much like that Amelia Earhart snipped off her Electra on her fatal world flight in 1937. We all hope SAC crews will not make this mistake!

Cockpit of Boeing E-4A Command Post.

Cessna AT-17 Bobcat. (courtesy Cessna)

Cessna T-50 Bobcat

Despite its official appellation of "Bobcat," Cessna's T-50 is perhaps more widely referred to as the "Bamboo Bomber" because of its spruce frame and fabric covering. Making its debut in 1939, the Bobcat served with the USAAF as the UC-78 (utility) and AT-17 (advanced trainer), and with the Navy as the JRC-1.

Compared to its twin-engine training stable-mate, the Beech 18, the Bobcat was lighter, slower, and shorter of range. It was, however, less expensive to produce and operate, and was considered "more expendable" to inevitable training accidents.

Powered by a pair of Jacobs or Lycoming radials, a number of the little twin Cessnas are extant and flying today, and are sought after by antique aircraft buffs and warbirders.

AT-17 panel. (courtesy Cessna)

163

Cessna 0-1 Bird Dog. (courtesy Cessna)

Cessna 0-1 Bird Dog

The Bird Dog, developed from Cessna's popular 170 line of aircraft, first appeared in 1950 and entered service with the U.S. Army as the L-19 (L for Liason). Powered by a Continental 0-470 of 213 hp and capable of 115 mph, the Bird Dog saw extensive service in Korea as a reconnaissance/observation aircraft and artillery spotter. More than 3300 were built in a production run which lasted through 1959.

Redesignated 0-1 in the 1960s, the Bird Dog, like other Korean War veteran aircraft, was again called to action in Vietnam. There, along with Cessna's 0-2 and Rockwell's 0V-10, the 0-1 was used in the hairy and dangerous FAC (Forward Air Controller) mission, flying "low and slow" to call in precision airstrikes by fighter-bombers. When Vietnam fell in 1975, one Vietnamese officer loaded his family into an 0-1 and flew them to safety aboard a U. S. Navy carrier.

Compare the Bird Dog's tandem seating and stick control with the cockpit of its civilian 170 brother on page 107.

Cessna 0-1E panel. (courtesy Cessna)

Cessna T-37. (courtesy Cessna)

Cessna T-37

Sometimes called the "Tweety Bird" and the "Six Thousand Pound Dog Whistle" due to the distinctive sound of its two Continental J69 engines, Cessna's T-37 was the Air Force's first jet aircraft designed from the ground up as a trainer. First flown in 1954, the last of 1,268 T-37s was delivered in 1977.

A light attack aircraft, the A-37 Dragonfly, was derived from the trainer, 39 A-37As being converted from T-37B trainers, and a further 577 A-37Bs manufactured. The A-37B, which saw successful service in Vietnam, was up-engined with General Electric J85 turbojets which permitted a near-doubling of the aircraft's takeoff weight to 12,000 pounds and allowed the Dragonfly to carry over 5000 pounds of ordnance on eight underwing hardpoints.

Cockpit of Cessna T-37. (courtesy Cessna)

Curtiss P-1B Hawk. (courtesy Francis H. Dean collection via Christy)

Curtiss P-1 Hawk

The U.S. Army bought a total of 247 Hawk biplanes from 1925 to 1932; all but one were modified versions of the basic P-1 or P-6 airframes. The first Hawk order was for fifteen airplanes, including the XP-1, s/n 25-410, nine P-1s, and five P-2s. The XP-1 went to McCook Field, the Army's air research and test center, and remained there as an engine test bed. It was raced in 1926, fitted with an inverted air-cooled Liberty engine, and it became the XP-17 in 1930 with the installation of an experimental Curtiss V-1460 inverted air-cooled V-12 engine of 500 hp.

The nine P-1 Hawks, fitted with Curtiss V-1150 (D-12) engines, saw service with the 27th and 94th Pursuit Squadrons of the First Pursuit Group at Selfridge Field, Michigan. The improved P-1B was ordered in August 1926 and featured a new radiator, flares, and other minor modifications.

The Navy also received five P-1s, which they designated F6C-1s.

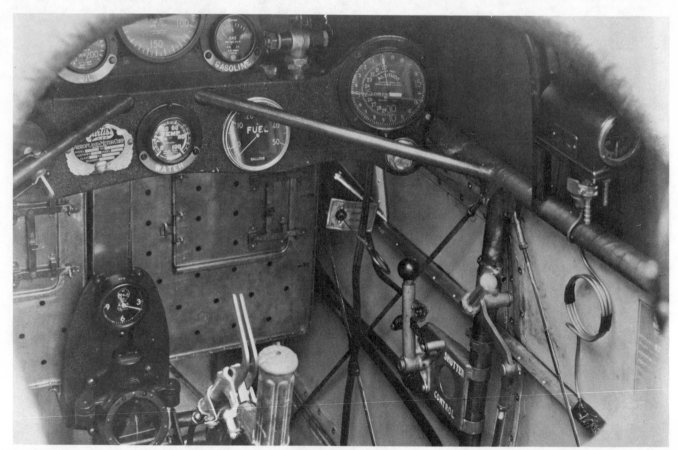

Cockpit of first P-1 Hawk, s/n 25-410. (courtesy USAF via Christy)

166

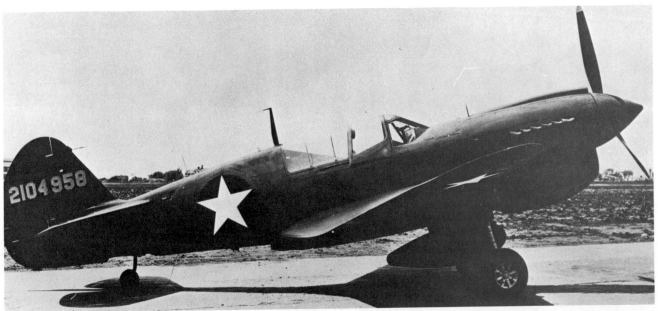

Curtiss P-40N-5 Warhawk. (courtesy USAF via Christy)

Curtiss P- 40 Warhawk

Like Germany's Messerschmitt 109, the Curtiss P-40 Warhawk traced its origins to a mid-1930s design, was first-line equipment at the beginning of World War II, and, despite obsolescence, continued to be modified and produced throughout that conflict. The P-40C, an early variant, was the mount of the American Volunteer Group, better known as the legendary Flying Tigers. Though not as nimble as its adversary, the Japanese Zero, the Warhawk was far more rugged and packed superior firepower.

Of the 13,736 Warhawks built, substantial numbers were supplied to Britain, Australia, New Zealand, and Russia. The ultimate production version was the P-40N, shown here, which incorporated a new, lightweight structure and other improvements in an attempt to extend the service life of the classic but aging aircraft. Further experiments produced the bubble-canopied XP-40Q, which failed to match the performance of the then-standard Mustangs and Thunderbolts; it did not reach production.

Panel of P-40N-15. (courtesy USAF Museum via Christy)

Douglas A-26B Invader. (courtesy McDonnell Douglas)

Douglas A-26B Invader

First flown on July 10, 1942, the Douglas A-26 Invader enjoyed a service record which can be matched by few aircraft. The only U.S. combat aircraft to see action in WWII, Korea, and Vietnam, the A-26 was designed to combine the best attributes of the B-25 Mitchell, the B-26 Marauder, and the A-20 Havoc. That this endeavor was successful is evident; Invaders were flying combat missions fully two decades after the aforementioned aircraft types had been phased out of the first-line U.S. inventory.

Arriving on the scene in time to fight in both Europe and the Pacific in the Second World War, the Invader's heyday was in Korea. Now redesignated B-26, both B (gun nose) and C (glass nose) versions were used as night "intruders" to disrupt and destroy North Korean supply lines, roads, depots, and bases. The Invader returned to service in Vietnam in the early '60s, and flew with the USAF and VNAF. These Invaders were designated B-26K, and had been modified and strengthened by the On-Mark Engineering Company, a firm which had specialized in converting surplus Invaders into plush and swift executive transports. A number of Invaders fly on today in private hands, in both "stock" and "custom" versions.

Powered by reliable Pratt & Whitney R-2800 engines, the fastest of the Invaders (A-26C) could top 370 mph and had a range of 1400 miles. Aside from U.S. and Vietnamese service, Invaders also equipped the air forces of Brazil, Chile, Columbia, Cuba, the Dominican Republic, Guatemala, Mexico, Nicaragua, Peru, France, Turkey, the Congo, Laos, and Saudi Arabia. Of particular interest is the fact that Invaders flew and fought on both sides during the disastrous Bay of Pigs fiasco.

Douglas A-26B cockpit. (courtesy McDonnell Douglas)

U.S. Navy A-1H (formerly AD-6). (courtesy McDonnell Douglas)

Douglas A-1 Skyraider

Built in seven major versions and nearly 40 sub-variants, the Skyraider first flew as the XBT2D-1 on March 18, 1945. Designed with the combat experience of WWII in mind, the Skyraider saw a quarter-century of service, including duty in both Korea and Vietnam.

Able to carry more than its own empty weight in fuel and ordnance on underwing stores, the Skyraider's reliability and versatility ensured it a place in the U.S. Navy well into an age in which it should have been thought an anachronism. Powered by the 3000-hp Wright R-3350 18-cylinder radial, the Skyraider was not phased out of the Navy's inventory until 1968, when it was replaced by the Grumman A-6. By this time, the "Spad" (as it was known to naval crews) had

racked up thousands of combat hours in Vietnam. The Skyraider's service record did not go unnoticed by the U.S. Air Force, which began to acquire A-1s in the 1960s to fight its own version of "brushfire ware." Aside from its excellence as an attack aircraft, the Air Force put the Skyraider's great range (up to 3000 miles) to good use on RESCAP missions, on which the A-1s would escort HH-53 "Jolly Green Giant" helicopters deep into enemy territory to retrieve downed pilots.

Once used by the air forces of France, Cambodia, Vietnam, Chad, and the United Kingdom, the Skyraider has at last given way to the jet age. A few have been restored and are flown for sport in the U.S.

Cockpit of USAF A-1J. (courtesy McDonnell Douglas)

A-4M Skyhawk II. (courtesy McDonnell Douglas)

Douglas (McDonnell-Douglas) A-4 Skyhawk

Sometimes known as "Heinemann's Hot Rod" (for Douglas chief engineer Ed Heinemann, who led its design team), the A-4 Skyhawk carried the Douglas reputation for outstanding attack aircraft into the jet age. Originally envisioned by Douglas as a lightweight fighter, the A-4 was shaped by Navy requirements for an attack aircraft and swiftly evolved to fill those needs. First flown in 1954, the last Skyhawk rolled off the production line in 1979. Over 3000 were built in versions from A to M, and Skyhawks saw extensive service with both Navy and Marine units in Vietnam. Two-seat versions, designated TA-4, were also built for the training role.

Besides U.S. service, the Skyhawk is a principal aircraft of the Israeli Air Force, and is also in use in Argentina, Australia, Chile, and New Zealand. The A-4 is also flown by the Navy's famous Blue Angels in their spectacular demonstrations.

A-4M panel. (courtesy McDonnell Douglas)

A-4M cockpit. (courtesy McDonnell Douglas)

Fairchild-Republic A-10. (courtesy USAF)

Fairchild Republic A-10

Fairchild Republic and Northrop were chosen in 1970 to build two prototypes for evaluation under the USAF's A-X program for a close-support aircraft. Three years later the A-10A was selected as the winner. First deliveries of production aircraft were made in 1976 to the 333rd Tactical Fighter Training Squadron at Davis-Monthan AFB, Arizona.

First operational A-10A unit is the 356th Tactical Fighter Wing at Myrtle Beach, South Carolina. The single-seater A-10As are equipped with Martin Marietta AN/AAS-35 Pave Penny laser target designation pods as standard equipment.

The A-10A uses a wide-chord, cantilevered, low wing with a deep airfoil section to provide a low wing loading, and carries a General Electric GAU-8/A Avenger 30mm seven-barrel cannon mounted in the nose, plus 11 pylons to carry a maximum of eight tons of ordnance, including Mk-82 and Mk-84 laser-guided bombs.

Combat speed of the A-10A carrying six Mk-82 bombs is 443 mph, while its operational radius for close air support and escort, 2-hour loiter and 20-minute reserve, is 288 miles; ferry range is 2647 miles. The cockpit photo shows a screen at upper right, which displays the view the missile "sees" with its infrared tracking system.

Cockpit of A-10. (courtesy Fairchild Republic)

General Dynamics F-16s of the 8th TFW "Wolf Pack;" based at Kunsan, Korea, the 8th is the first USAF unit to deploy the F-16 overseas. (courtesy General Dynamics)

General Dynamics
F-16 Fighting Falcon

Developed originally as a lightweight, low-cost air combat fighter, the F-16 with, the addition of air-to-surface and all-weather radar and navigation capabilities, has become a true multi-role fighter. Powered by the same Pratt & Whitney F100 afterburning turbofan used in the F-15, the F-16 is (or will be) in service with the USAF, Israel, Egypt, Belgium, Denmark, Norway, and the Netherlands.

The F-16's cockpit is among the most advanced ever seen in any aircraft. The force-sensing sidestick controller is linked with a fully-electronic "fly by wire" flight control system, giving the pilot quick, precise maneuvering ability. Additionally, the F-16 pilot can accomplish all combat tasks without removing his hands from the stick and throttle. The throttle incorporates six switches and the radar curser control; mounted on the stick are the trim switch, four weapon/radar switches, and a gun trigger. In his 30-degree reclined seat, the pilot can withstand G forces longer and use the aircraft's 9G maneuver capability to full advantage. The F-16's one-piece bubble canopy gives the pilot a virtually unlimited view of his combat environment.

F-16 cockpit. (courtesy General Dynamics)

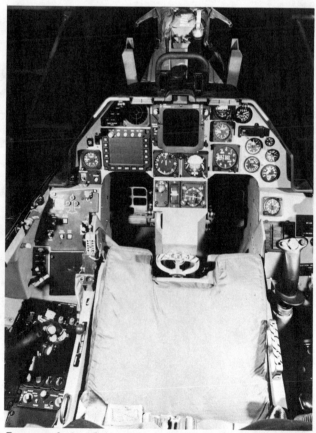

Rear cockpit of two-place F-16B. (courtesy General Dynamics)

Grumman F4F-3 Wildcat. (courtesy Grumman Aerospace)

F4F-4 cockpit. (courtesy Grumman Aerospace)

Grumman F4F Wildcat

While it became the first successful monoplane carrier fighter, Grumman's F4F Wildcat actually began life as a biplane. The Navy ordered development of the XF4F-1 in March, 1936, as a biplane—a backup aircraft should the new Brewster F2A monoplane (also ordered in that year) prove unsatisfactory in carrier operations. Within six months, however, the Navy changed its mind and had Grumman proceed with the design—now called the XF4F-2—as a monoplane. By 1939, Grumman had developed the aircraft into the XF4F-3, the first of a long line of Wildcats.

Ironically, while the Brewster F2A's career was spectacularly undistinguished, the Wildcat went on to equip all U.S. carrier fighter squadrons by 1942. While outclassed in air combat by the Japanese Zero, the Wildcat was the only American carrier-based fighter for the first 18 months of the war and ac-

counted for 905 aerial victories while participating in such naval battles as Wake Island, Coral Sea, and Midway.

With the appearance of Grumman's superior F6F Hellcat in 1943, Grumman was requested to concentrate on production of the newer aircraft. Wildcats were still needed for duty on small escort carriers and MAC ships, however, and Wildcat production was carried on by the Eastern Aircraft Division of General Motors. Designated the FM-1, the GM-built version was similar to Grumman's F4F-4. Eastern also produced an improved version, the FM-2, which replaced the F4F's 1200-hp P & W R-1830 with the supercharged Wright R-1820 of 1350 hp.

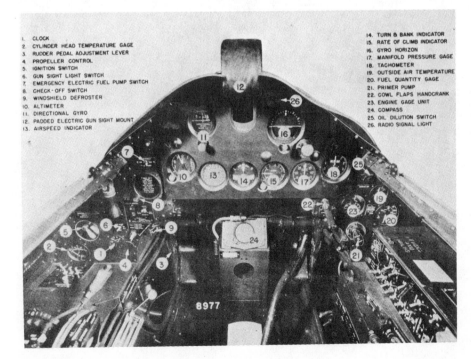

1. CLOCK
2. CYLINDER HEAD TEMPERATURE GAGE
3. RUDDER PEDAL ADJUSTMENT LEVER
4. PROPELLER CONTROL
5. IGNITION SWITCH
6. GUN SIGHT LIGHT SWITCH
7. EMERGENCY ELECTRIC FUEL PUMP SWITCH
8. CHECK-OFF SWITCH
9. WINDSHIELD DEFROSTER
10. ALTIMETER
11. DIRECTIONAL GYRO
12. PADDED ELECTRIC GUN SIGHT MOUNT
13. AIRSPEED INDICATOR

14. TURN & BANK INDICATOR
15. RATE OF CLIMB INDICATOR
16. GYRO HORIZON
17. MANIFOLD PRESSURE GAGE
18. TACHOMETER
19. OUTSIDE AIR TEMPERATURE
20. FUEL QUANTITY GAGE
21. PRIMER PUMP
22. COWL FLAPS HANDCRANK
23. ENGINE GAGE UNIT
24. COMPASS
25. OIL DILUTION SWITCH
26. RADIO SIGNAL LIGHT

F4F-4 instrument panel. (courtesy Grumman Aerospace)

Grumman F6F-5 Hellcats. (courtesy Grumman Aerospace)

Grumman F6F Hellcat

Grumman's successor to the F4F Wildcat, the F6F Hellcat, incorporated improvements in speed, range, maneuverability, and power in response to the threat of advanced Japanese fighters, most notably the Zero. The prototype XF6F-3 first flew in July, 1942; by January, 1943, Hellcats were operational with VF-9 aboard the USS *Essex*. Within a year, the F6F had become the standard U.S. carrier fighter, and remained so for the rest of WWII. Of 12,274 Hellcats built, virtually all were of just two variants, the F6F-3 and F6F-5. Night fighter (F6F-3N and F6F-5N) and photo-recon (F6F-5P) versions were also produced.

In combat, the F6F achieved a kill-to-loss ratio of over 19 to one, and accounted for more than 5000 aerial victories. Hellcats were the mounts of many Navy and Marine aces, including the Navy's top-scoring David McCampbell (34 victories).

After the war, many Hellcats were turned over to Naval Air Reserve units, and others were converted to F6F-3K and F6F-5K drones. Fitted with radio control equipment, these pilotless drones were used for a variety of tasks, including "flying bomb" missions against bridges and other targets in Korea.

Grumman F6F-5 cockpit. (courtesy Grumman Aerospace)

Grumman F7F-3 Tigercat. (courtesy Grumman Aerospace)

Grumman F7F Tigercat

Designed for use on the 45,000-ton *Midway* class carriers, Grumman's F7F was the Navy's first operational twin-engined shipboard aircraft and the first fighter to successfully use a tricycle landing gear aboard a carrier. Although ordered in June 1941 and first flown in December 1943, the Tigercat arrived at the front too late to see combat, equipping a few land-based Marine squadrons in the final days of the Pacific war.

Powered by P & W R-2800s, the fastest of the Tigercat variants could hit 435 mph at 20,600 feet. The F7F was built in -1, -2N, -3, -3N, and -4N versions, the N variants being two-place night fighters with redesigned noses housing radar. Single-seat versions carried unusually heavy armament: four 20mm cannon and four .50-cal. machine guns.

After being withdrawn from service, a number of Tigercats found new jobs as "borate bombers," dropping water and retardant chemicals on forest fires in the 1960s and '70s.

1. Carburetor Air Control Switch
2. Oil Cooler Exit Duct Door Switches
3. Cowl Flaps Control Switch
4. Propeller Feathering Controls
5. Propeller Feathering Circuit Breaker Reset Button
6. Fuel Pressure Warning Light
7. Auxiliary Fuel Pump Control
8. Water Injection Control
9. Wing Fold Safety Lock Control
10. Fuel Tank Selector Valve Control
11. Wing Drop. Tanks Solenoid Valve Control Switch
12. Engine Selector Valve
13. Fuel Quantity Gage
14. Cockpit Heater Selector
15. L.G. (Nose and Main) Emergency Dump Controls
16. Oxygen Flow Blinker
17. Oxygen Regulator
18. Emergency Brake Air Bottle Filler Plug
19. Emergency Brake Air Bottle Gage
20. Control Stick Grip
21. Main Instrument Panel
22. Gun Charger Controls
23. Rudder and Brake Pedal
24. IFF Control Switch (Replaced by Radio Altimeter on Night Fighters)
25. Cockpit Hood Control
26. Cockpit Hood Control Release
27. Oxygen Cylinder Control
28. Pilot's Switch Box
29. Hydraulic Hand Pump

F7F cockpit. (courtesy Grumman Aerospace)

Grumman F8F Bearcat. (courtesy Grumman Aerospace)

F8F panel and gunsight. (courtesy Grumman Aerospace)

Grumman F8F Bearcat

Grumman's F8F was designed after learning the lessons of air combat in the Pacific war and was meant to beat the Japanese fighter aircraft at their own game. Employing the best features of both the Japanese (light weight, high maneuverability) and American (massive horsepower, heavy firepower) design philosophies, the Bearcat was intended to be the smallest practical airframe which could be built around Pratt & Whitney's reliable 2000-hp R-2800.

Unfortunately, the F8F never got a chance to prove itself at its intended task, arriving too late to see service in WWII. By the time of the Korean war, the Bearcat had been replaced as a first-line fighter by the new jets and was not considered rugged enough to serve as a fighter-bomber, as did the F4U. The Royal Thai and Vietnamese Air Forces operated F8Fs for a time, and they did see some action with the French in Indochina.

Not until the era of Unlimited air racers in the '60s and '70s did the Bearcat find its niche, a small number doing battle with the Mustangs, Lightnings, and Sea Furies at Reno and Mojave. The most successful of these was unquestionably Darryl Greenamyer's N1111L *Conquest One*, which, apart from its numerous racing victories, also set a world's prop-driven landplace speed record. N1111L is now in the possession of the National Air and Space Museum.

F8F left console and throttle quadrant. (courtesy Grumman Aerospace)

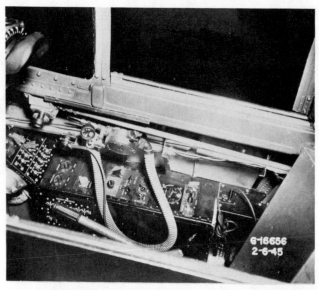

F8F right console. (courtesy Grumman Aerospace)

176

Grumman F9F-2 Panther. (courtesy Grumman Aerospace)

Grumman F9F Panther

Grumman's first jet fighter for the Navy was the F9F Panther, which made its maiden flight on December 21, 1947. By the time the Korean War broke out, the Panther was operational as first-line equipment, and it shared duties in that action with McDonnell's F2H Banshee. Although Panthers were credited with the destruction of several MiG-15s, the introduction of the F-86 into the war to counter the MiG threat relegated the F9F (along with the Air Force's F-80 and F-84) to mainly the fighter-bomber role. The Panther proved particularly adaptable to this service, carrying bombs and/or rockets on six or eight underwing hardpoints.

Panther production totaled 1,385; the principal variants were the F9F-2, powered by the 5000-lb thrust P & W J42P-6, and the F9F-5, powered by the J48P-2 of 6250 lb thrust.

F9F-2 panel. (courtesy Grumman Aerospace)

F9F-2 left console. (courtesy Grumman Aerospace)

F9F-2 right console. (courtesy Grumman Aerospace)

Grumman F-14 Tomcat. (courtesy USN via Christy)

Grumman F-14 Tomcat

The newest of Grumman's fighting "cats" for the Navy, the F-14 Tomcat entered service in 1974 and flew its first operational missions in fighter escort duty during the evacuation from Southeast Asia in 1975. Charged with the aerial defense of the fleet, the Tomcat's capabilities also include strike force protection, combat air patrol, and tactical air-to-ground attack.

The Tomcat's variable-geometry wings sweep from 20 to 68 degrees, and give the fighter an unusually wide performance envelope. Its top speed exceeds Mach 2.3. The F-14 carries highly sophisticated avionics and electronic weapons system, including the AN/AWG-9 fire control and target illuminating radar, which can track up to 24 targets simultaneously while guiding as many as six Hughes AIM-54A Phoenix missiles to their targets.

F-14 Pilot's panel. (courtesy Grumman Aerospace)

F-14 Flight Officer's panel. (courtesy Grumman Aerospace)

Hughes AH-64 Apache. (courtesy Hughes Helicopters)

AH-64 pilot display. (courtesy Hughes Helicopters)

Hughes AH-64 Apache

The Hughes AH-64 Apache is the first Army attack helicopter to be developed specifically for the day/night, adverse weather anti-armor mission with emphasis on the ability to fight, survive, and live with the troops in the frontline battle environment. The primary weapon of the AH-64 is the Rockwell Hellfire antitank missile, which is capable of disabling all known armor threats and allows multiple target engagement. Suppressive firepower is provided by 2.75-inch rockets and a 30mm automatic cannon.

Hughes engineers paid particular attention to crew survivability in the design of the AH-64. It is estimated that the Apache's crew has a 95 percent probability of surviving a crash at an impact rate of 42 feet per second.

Lockheed P-38J and photo-recon F-5 Lightnings. (courtesy Lockheed)

Lockheed P-38 Lightning

One of the most distinctive fighter aircraft of World War II, the Lockheed P-38 was designed to meet a 1936 Air Corps specification calling for a high-altitude interceptor with a speed of 360 mph at 20,000 feet and the ability to fly at full throttle for one hour. Kelly Johnson's design team produced the twin Allison-engined, twin-boom fighter that would see combat with 23 fighter groups in Europe, the Mediterranean, and the Pacific.

Until the advent of the P-51B Mustang, the Lightning was the only Allied fighter with sufficient range to escort the 8th Air Force's heavy bombers to targets deep in Germany, and the P-38's twin-engine reliability was looked upon with favor by pilots flying long overwater missions in the Pacific. Lightnings were flown by America's two top-scoring aces of all time, Maj. Richard Bong (40 victories) and Maj. Thomas McGuire (38 victories); Lightnings shot down and killed Japanese Admiral Yamamoto; Lightnings were selected, because of their distinctive planform, to fly escort for the *Overlord* armada which invaded Hitler's Europe.

The P-38 was also built in photo-recon (F-5), night fighter (P-38M), and bombing ("Droop Snoot") variants. Note in the cockpit photo that the Lightning's control system utilized a control wheel instead of the nearly universal stick of fighter aircraft.

P-38 Lightning cockpit. (courtesy Lockheed)

Lockheed P-80B. (courtesy Lockheed)

Lockheed P-80 Shooting Star

World War II's most successful jet fighter was born when Lockheed was asked in 1943 to build a single-seater around the deHavilland Goblin engine imported from England. The prototype was completed in a record 143 days and first flew on January 9, 1944 as the XP-80, the first American plane to top 500 mph.

While the P-80 Shooting Star never saw action in WWII, subsequent models were battle tested. The P-80B pictured here came out in 1947 with a pilot ejection seat, underwing rocket launchers and other innovations. P-80Cs flew close to 100,000 sorties over Korea. On November 8, 1950, a P-80C destroyed a MiG-15 in history's first all-jet air battle.

The P-80C had a V_{max} of 580 mph at 7000 feet, cruised at 439 mph, and landed at 122 mph. Range was 1380 miles.

Lockheed P-80 cockpit. (courtesy Lockheed)

Lockheed L-100-30 Super Hercules.

Lockheed Hercules

Lockheed's high-wing, low-slung C-130 Hercules has become a "workhorse of the jet age" with more than 1600 built in many models and derivatives. About 1000 were delivered to the USAF; others went to the U.S. Navy, Marines, and Coast Guard. C-130s fly under the flags of 46 nations into ports from Abu Dhabi to Jakarta and McMurdo Station in Antarctica, where they are fitted with skis.

As a commercial transport the Hercules flies in two versions, the L-100-20 and the L-100-30. Trans-

america Airlines operates a dozen Super Hercules on regular military cargo flights for the U.S. military in Europe and Africa. The first production C-130A flew at Lockheed-Georgia early in 1955. One Hercules set a world record for long-distance nonstop, non-refueled turboprop flight when an Aerospace Rescue and Recovery Service crew flew from Taiwan 8790 miles to Illinois in 21 hours 12 minutes. Perhaps the Hercules' most famous and daring exploit to date was the transportation of the Israeli commando team on the Entebbe rescue raid of 1976.

Lockheed L-100-30 Cockpit.

Lockheed F-104G Starfighter. (courtesy Lockheed)

Lockheed F-104 Starfighter

Lockheed's F-104 Starfighter is recognized as having the smallest and thinnest wings of any American jet. Design began in November, 1952, as Lockheed Model 83. The first prototype to fly hit Mach 1.79 on February 7, 1954. Subsequent versions used more powerful engines, enlarged fins, and greater firepower. The Mach 2 F-104G first flew October 5, 1960, and has room to carry a one-ton nuclear store.

More than one thousand F-104Gs have been built for such NATO nations as West Germany, The Netherlands, Belgium, and Italy. Canadair also has built 104 for Denmark, Greece, Norway, and Turkey.

The first two-seater Starfighter, the F-104B, first flew early in 1957, and 26 went to the Nationalist Chinese Air Force in Taiwan. The two-seater F-104D has been built for the USAF, Japan's Air Self-Defense Force, and the RCAF.

The F-104 continues in production at Aeritalia for the Italian Air Force as the single-seat F-104S. Equipment includes an integrated electronics system and an autopilot with stick-steering, including modes for preselecting and holding altitude, speed, heading and constant rate of turn, multi-purpose radar for air-to-air intercept, ground and contour mapping, and terrain avoidance for low-level runs.

Cockpit of F-104C Starfighter. (courtesy Lockheed)

Lockheed C-141 StarLifter. (courtesy Lockheed)

Lockheed C-141 StarLifter

Lockheed's C-141A StarLifter first flew on December 17, 1963, the 60th Anniversary of the Wright Brothers' first flight at Kitty Hawk. It was designed to carry up to 154 troops in full battle gear, 127 paratroops, or 80 casualty stretchers with 8 medical attendants. The first full squadron began operations as a component of the 1501st Air Transport Wing of USAF Military Air Transport Service (MATS) from Travis AFB in 1965.

As an air freighter, the StarLifter can carry a complete Minutemen ICBM container weighing 88,000 pounds. In January, 1977, a stretched version, the YC-141B, first flew, fitted with inflight refueling equipment inside the fuselage, 23 feet longer. The new model was fitted with improved wing root fairings to decrease drag, providing higher cruise speeds and lower fuel consumption. The fairings also changed the lift distribution, permitting an increased payload without affecting the fatigue life of the wing.

The cockpit photo shows a C-141 flight crew at stations on a flight to McMurdo Sound in the Antarctic during a resupply mission.

Cockpit of C-141 StarLifter. (courtesy USAF)

Lockheed U-2. (courtesy Lockheed)

Lockheed U-2

Lockheed's super-secret U-2 spy plane was designed for strategic reconnaissance and other clandestine missions over Communist territory. It was first flown in 1955 and was optimized for flying at altitudes, which at the time rendered it immune to interception.

The requirement resulted in sacrifices in structural strength. With its light airframe and a wing with an amazing aspect ratio of 14.3:1, the U-2 was virtually a powered sailplane. The first three production examples, U-2A, with an 11,200-pound static thrust J57-P-37A engine, were accepted by USAF in mid-1956. By that time others had been delivered for clandestine operations by civilian pilots, including Gary Powers, who was shot down over Russia.

The U-2B, introduced in 1959, used a bigger engine and wet wings holding 1112 Imperial gallons of fuel. Fifty single-seat U-2s were built, some being used for high-altitude air sampling, gust research, radar calibration, etc. Five U-2Ds; a two-seater version, were built. The U-2's V_{max} is 528 mph; ceiling is above 90,000 feet; and range is 4000 miles.

Lockheed U-2 CT cockpit. (courtesy Lockheed)

Lockheed C-5A Galaxy. (courtesy Lockheed via Christy)

Lockheed C-5A Galaxy

The largest jet transport aircraft in the world, Lockheed's C-5A Galaxy was developed to meet a military call for an aircraft with a gross weight twice that of the C-141. Lockheed was selected for the project in October, 1965; the prototype first flew in June, 1968. The Military Airlift Command received the first of its 81 Galaxies in December, 1969 and the last in March, 1973.

Weighing 326,962 pounds empty, the C5-A has a maximum takeoff weight in excess of 768,000 pounds. The photo shows a typical Galaxy load: the aircraft can carry 256,000 pounds 2900 miles nonstop at 530 mph and land in just 5000 feet.

C5-A cockpit. In the copilot's seat is USAF Col. McCormick, who headed the Galaxy flight test program. (courtesy Lockheed)

McDonnell Douglas F-15 Eagle.(courtesy McDonnell Douglas)

McDonnell Douglas F-15 Eagle

First flight of the McDonnell Douglas F-15A was made in July, 1972, and by July, 1977, 208 Eagles had been delivered, of which 172 were operational at Nellis AFB, Nevada; Luke Field, Arizona; Langley, Virginia; and Bitburg, Germany. Others have gone to the Israeli Air Force and to Saudi Arabia.

Designed as an air superiority fighter, the Eagle has proven its worth also for air-to-ground missions. Powered with two Pratt & Whitney F100-PW-100 tur-

bofans of 25,000 pounds static thrust, the Eagle has variable geometry air inlets. The single pilot has long-range Doppler radar for tracking small, high-speed targets at all altitudes down to treetop level, and computer controlled weaponry. For dogfighting, the radar automatically acquires the target on a head-up display, enabling the pilot to score a kill without taking his eyes off the enemy.

Max takeoff weight is 56,000 pounds, V_{max} is Mach 2.5+, range with FAST pack fuel load 3450 miles.

F-15 Eagle cockpit panel.

187

North American T-6 Texan.(courtesy Rockwell International)

North American T-6 cockpit instruction panel, a training device. (courtesy U.S. Air Force)

North American T-6 Texan

The T-6 Texan two-place advanced trainer was the classroom for most of the Allied pilots who flew in World War II. Called the SNJ by the Navy and the Harvard by the RAF and RCAF, the T-6 was designed as a transition trainer between basic trainers and first-line tactical aircraft. In all, the T-6 trained several hundred thousand pilots in 34 different countries; a total of 15,495 were built.

A pilot's airplane, the Texan could roll, Immelmann, loop, spin, snap, and vertical roll. It was designed to give the best possible training in all types of tactics, from ground strafing to bombardment and aerial dogfighting, and could be outfitted with such versatile equipment as bomb racks, blind flying instrumentation, gun and standard cameras, fixed and flexible guns, and other military equipment.

Though most famous as a trainer, T-6 "Mosquitos" were used as forward air controllers in the Korean war. Many are flown for sport today.

North American B-25D Mitchell.(courtesy Rockwell International)

North American B-25 Mitchell

The B-25 Mitchell is assured a place in history by virtue of its use in the famous carrier-based "Doolittle Raid" of April 18, 1942. Yet this twin-tailed, twin engined (R-2600 Wright Cyclones) medium bomber also became known as one of the most useful and versatile combat aircraft ever designed. Produced throughout World War II, a total of 9,816 Mitchells were delivered in A, B, C, D G, H, and J variants. A photorecon version was designated F-10.

The B-25 was used extensively in the Pacific as a low-level attack aircraft, the G and H models packing a 75mm cannon in the nose and the "hard-nose" J models carrying no less than 14 forward-firing .50-cal. machine guns. Equipping land-based Marine patrol bomber squadrons, the Mitchell was known as the PBJ.

The war's end did not stop the Mitchell's career. Many were converted to TB-25 trainers and others soldiered on as squadron "hacks" until well into the '50s. Still others found their way into civilian hands and were used as executive transports, aerial firefighters, Hollywood camera ships, and utility aircraft.

B-25 Mitchell cockpit. (courtesy USAF)

North American P-51D Mustang. (courtesy Rockwell International)

North American P-51D Mustang

Arguably the best fighter aircraft to see combat with any nation in World War II, North American's Mustang arose from inauspicious beginnings. Approached by the British Purchasing Commission in 1940 to produce the Curtiss P-40, North American President James H. "Dutch" Kindelberger and Vice-President John Atwood had a better idea: they would design and build their own fighter—a superior fighter—in the same time and at the same cost it would have taken them to tool up for P-40 production. The prototype NA-73X, the first of 14,501 Mustangs, was rolled out on August 30, 1940, after just 117 days of fevered design and construction.

The Mustang proved to be a superb low-level fighter and attack aircraft with the Allison engine, but it was after the substitution of the Rolls-Royce Merlin 65 (produced under license in the U.S. by Packard as the V-1650) that its full potential was reached. Possessing the longest range of any single-engined U.S. fighter, the P-51 was able to escort the 8th Air Force's heavy bombers all the way to the very heart of Germany.

Mustangs also served admirably in the Mediterranean, CBI, and Pacific theaters; later, despite their vulnerable liquid-cooled engines, they went on to perform yeoman service in the fighter-bomber role in Korea. The definitive version, the P-51D shown here, eventually equipped many air forces of the Free World, some serving on into the 1970s.

Somewhere around 100 Mustangs survive; they are among the most popular of warbirds and are the mainstay of Unlimited class air racing.

P-51D panel. (courtesy U.S. Air Force)

P-51D panel and right consoles. (courtesy U.S. Air Force)

North American F-86E Sabres. (courtesy Rockwell International)

North American F-86 Sabre

"To the victor belong the spoils." This quote from the political arena is particularly applicable to the design of the F-86 Sabre. North American's first (1944) design proposal for the XP-86 featured unswept wings (like NA's FJ-1 for the Navy) and was, in effect, a turbojet-engined Mustang. When this design failed to live up to the Army Air Force requirements for speed, North American engineers returned to the drawing boards, this time utilizing captured German studies documenting the effects and benefits of the swept wing. The resultant design became the famous F-86 Sabre.

Like its Mustang predecessor, the Sabre was a thoroughbred. It was produced in eleven major variants, and eventually was flown by the air forces of no less than 31 nations. The "D" version ("Dog Sabre") featured afterburner, intercept radar, electronic fire control, and all-rocket armament; the fighter-bomber

"H" had the capability of delivering atomic weapons, toss-bombing them via the Low Altitude Bombing System (LABS).

The Sabre's heyday was in Korea, the F-86As, Es, and Fs of the 4th and 51st Fighter Interceptor Wings racking up a kill ratio exceeding 8-to-1 (14-to-1, according to some sources) over their Iron Curtain counterparts, the MiG-15s flown by North Korean and Chinese Communist (and, reportedly, Soviet) pilots. This figure is even more impressive when considering that the MiGs had superior numbers, superior rate-of-climb, higher service ceiling, and the "home field" advantage.

One U.S. Air Force pilot paid fitting tribute to the Sabre in the early '70's after his first flight in the new F-15 Eagle: "This is the first 'dogfighter' we've had in the inventory since the F-86."

Cockpit of early F-86A-1. (courtesy U.S. Air Force)

North American OV-10As of USAF and Marines.

North American OV-10A

North American Aviation bid against eight other plane makers in a U. S. Navy competition for a light armed reconnaissance airplane (LARA) specifically suited to counterinsurgency missions. Their entry, NA-300, won in August, 1964, and seven prototypes were built by the company's Columbus Division as the YOV-10A Bronco. A number of modifications were made as a result of flight tests with the prototypes, resulting in six versions—the OV-10A, OV-10B, OV-10C, OV-10D, OV-10E, and OV-10F.

The OV-10A first flew August 6, 1967, and within two years the U.S. Marine Corps had 114 in service, with 18 on loan to the Navy. Missions included light armed reconnaissance, helicopter escort, and forward air control duties. The USAF also had 157 OV-10As employed in forward air control and limited quick response ground support pending arrival of tactical fighters.

Equipment installed by LTV included a stabilized night periscope sight, a combination laser rangefinder and target illuminator, a LORAN receiver and a Lear Siegler LORAN coordinate converter, enabling the pilot to strike the target directly, or fire a laser-seeking missile at it. Powered with two AirResearch turboprops, the OV-10A could fly level without weapons at 281 mph.

North American OV-10A cockpit. (courtesy USAF)

Northrop P-61 Black Widow.

Northrop P-61 Black Widow

The XP-61 Northrop Black Widow first flew on May 21, 1942, as the first American combat ship specifically designed as a night fighter. As big as a medium bomber, it carried two 2000-hp Pratt & Whitney Wasps, twin rudders on twin tail booms and a tricycle gear. The central nacelle had a radar nose, a pilot's cabin with radar operator above and behind him, and a gunner's enclosure.

Retractable ailerons permitted full-span flaps and armament consisted of four 20mm fixed guns below the fuselage and four .50-calibers in a remotely controlled top turret. Black Widows scored their first kill on July 7, 1944, in the South Pacific.

Fitted with R-2800-77 turbocharged engines of 2100 hp, the XP-61D had a V_{max} of 430 mph at 30,000 feet, a 43,000-foot ceiling, and 1050-mile range at 197 mph or 3000 miles max.

P-61A cockpit.

Northrop F-89D.

Northrop F-89 Scorpion

Northrop Corporation built a total of 1052 F-89 Scorpion two-seat, all-weather interceptor fighters, including prototypes, one XF-89, one YF-89A, eighteen F-89As, thirty F-89Bs, 164 F-89Cs, 682 F-89Ds, and 156 F-89Hs.

The Scorpion was the most successful postwar long-range all-weather interceptor. The first prototype flew on August 16, 1948, powered by two Allison J-35 jets, under a thin wing against the fuselage. From 1957 to 58 the Scorpion was phased out of service with the USAF's Air Defense Command but some remained in service with the Air National Guard.

The F-89D was modified as the F-89J by installation of Hughes MG-12 fire control, provision of pylons underwing for two AIR-2A Genie nuclear-tipped rockets, plus pylons for up to four AIM-4 Falcon AAMs. Wingtips were modified to take fuel or FFAR pods. V_{max} was 628 mph at 10,500 feet; climb was 8300 fpm; ceiling was over 49,000 feet; and range was 994 miles.

F-89 cockpit.

194

Northrop Tiger II F-5F.

Northrop F-5F Tiger II

In 1970 the F-5E won a competition by the U.S. Government to select an International Fighter Aircraft (IFA) to succeed the Northrop F-5A, with production estimated to eventually exceed 1500 aircraft. Called Tiger II, the new model came in two versions—the single-seat F-5E and the tandem two-seater F-5F, with a longer fuselage. First flight of the F-5F was on September 25, 1974.

Power is supplied to the F-5F by two 5000-pound thrust General Electric J85-GE-21A turbojets, giving it a maximum speed at 36,000 feet of Mach 1.63. The cockpit and electronics bay are pressurized, heated and air-conditioned. F-5F electronics and equipment include: AN/ARC-150 UHF/AM command, AN/AIC-18 or -25 interphone set, AN/APX-72 IFF/SIF transponder, TS1843/APX transponder test set, AN/ARN-84 TACAN, AN/ARC-157 fire control radar, AN/ASG-29 lead computing optical sight, AN/ARA-50 UHF/DF, and SST-181X X-band beacon skyspot. Optional equipment includes assisted takeoff rockets; photo-reconnaissance nose; in-flight refueling system; pylon jettison conversion kits; improved-performance ejection seats; anti-skid brakes; and chaff/flare countermeasures package.

Cockpit of Northrop Tiger II F-5F. (courtesy USAF)

195

Republic F-105F Thunderchiefs, with F-100. (courtesy USAF via Christy)

Republic F-105 Thunderchief

Republic's F-105 Thunderchief was America's first military aircraft designed from the start as a Tactical Air Force fighter/bomber. It was born in 1952 as Republic's Model AP-63. First to fly was the YF-105A, powered with a Pratt & Whitney J57-P-25, on October 22, 1955. A second model, the F-105B-1, flew on May 27, 1957, with a more powerful J75-P-3 engine and incorporation of the "area rule" fuselage design developed by NASA's Dr. Richard T. Whitcomb, also known as the "Coke bottle" or "wasp waist" shape.

The Thunderchief incorporated the first internal bomb bay used on a fighter, containing the MK-28 nuclear store, or four 750-pound bombs. The long fuselage (68 feet 2 inches) also holds all internal fuel, and petal-like dive brakes are installed behind the afterburner. Wings were swept back from root intakes with raked-forward lips. The most widely used Thunderchief was the F-105D all-weather model.

The F-105F first flew in 1963 as a two-seater trainer, of which 97 were built. The F-105F can undertake the same strike sorties as the F-105D, and uses the AN/ASG-19 Thunderstick fire control system including NASARR search and ranging radar. V_{max} is 1386 mph at 36,000 feet or 876 mph at sea level.

Cockpit of F-105F Thunderchief. (courtesy USAF)

Vought F4U-1D of the Confederate Air Force. (courtesy Vought Corporation)

Vought F4U Corsair

The Corsair's graceful inverted gull wing came about as the solution to a combination of problems involving propeller clearance, landing gear length and angle, and the requirement for folding wings for carrier storage. Happily, Vought's solution to these problems also resulted in an optimum right angle at the wing/fuselage junction, resulting in a minimum of drag.

The F4U was probably the best carrier fighter of WWII, but, ironically, was not approved by the Navy for shipboard operations until April 1944. Problems with stiff landing gear and pilot visibility prevented carrier qualification of the early Corsairs, which were assigned to land-based Navy and Marine units. The Corsair returned to service as a fighter-bomber in Korea with the improved F4U-4 and F4U-5 variants, and the type remained in production until 1953 when the last F4U-7s were built for France.

The cockpit photo shows an early "birdcage" F4U-1; the aircraft pictured in flight is an F4U-1D restored and operated by the Confederate Air Force.

Cockpit of early Vought F4U-1. (courtesy Vought Corporation)

Chapter 10
Air Carrier Cockpits

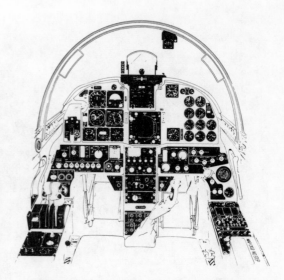

World War I had barely ended when America's aviation industry was faced with a massive problem—how best to switch over from wartime to peacetime production and operation of aircraft. Federal airways would have to be laid out, commercial passenger planes designed and built, and a concerted propaganda effort launched to educate the public in regard to the safety, convenience, and virtual necessity of travel by air for both business and pleasure.

Otto Praeger, Second Assistant Postmaster General, saw an immediate need for federal legislation to prevent "harrassment through legislative restrictions by the various States" and open the skies to well-regulated air commerce.

It was well and good to talk about converting such warplanes as the DeHavillands for mapping air routes, flying boats for coastal patrol, pursuit planes for air police duties, and Caproni and Handley Page machines for long-range cargo hauling, but a complete separation of military and civilian aviation was an obvious first step to development of air commerce.

Looking ahead, Praeger said: "I can think of no greater danger facing the airplane industry than to adapt its operation during the next ten, twenty, or thirty years of peace to the possible needs of the military in the event of war, and I can see no greater aid to insuring the development of the airplane industry than the development of airplanes for commercial uses and the unrestricted field to aeronautical engineers and builders to meet the needs of commerce."

Early, prewar efforts had in fact been made to get organized passenger-carrying moving through the skies. For the first three months of 1914, St. Petersburg-Tampa Airboat Line had operated between St. Petersburg and Tampa, Florida, 20 miles apart. A couple of small flying boats also made two round trips a day, when weather permitted and the demand warranted.

In 1918, however, the Post Office Department launched a scheduled airmail route between a Washington D.C. polo field and a New York race track. While the President and his Cabinet cheered, the first northbound mail plane took off, completely missed the route to New York, and finally landed on a farm in Maryland, nearly out of gas. The southbound flight did better: Lieutenants Torrey Webb and J.C. Edgerton found Philadelphia and transferred their load to a waiting plane. Within 3 hours 20 minutes they dumped the New York mail in Washington. By 1921, airmail pilots were following bonfires at night and railroads by day between New York and San Francisco in something over 33 hours. Two years later, searchlights illuminated the route between Dayton and Columbus, Ohio, 80 miles apart. By 1926 beacons stretched from coast to coast.

Adcock Radio Ranges

This was all well and good, but something better was needed: navigation equipment in the cockpit by which pilots could follow radio signals instead of bonfires and railroad tracks.

Prior to World War II, the Civil Aeronautics Administration established a Radio Range System of "Adcock" square ranges that offered pilots four "beams" to follow. Orientation using these ranges was a fine art, and pilots became proficient at locating which quadrant of a range they were in simply by listening to the DIT-DAH or DAH-DIT signals in their headsets while they flew through 90-degree turns and other maneuvers.

All that was changed with inauguration of the Federal Airway System of VOR stations, which pilots could follow simply by watching a needle and noting which way it pointed. Today's air carrier cockpits are a far cry from those of the early air transports, as we have noted in earlier chapters.

Improved electronic airways development led to

early use of multiple NAV/COMM systems for combined reception of VHF navigation and communications signals, along with LF, UHF, ADF, TACAN, and other black boxes, including more precise DME units to measure distance instantly from a station with accuracy.

As more sophisticated equipment became available, the airlines installed advanced navigation instrument systems that present the pilot with pictorial-symbolic plan views by combining the Course Indicator with the Gyro Compass. There quickly followed Integrated Flight Director Systems, Horizon Director Indicators, Course Deviation Indicators, and other goodies.

Soon the Flight Director System was coupled with vertical reading performance tapes to produce a system whereby the pilot need only match horizontal and vertical lines, highly superior for monitoring engine performance in multi-engined transports.

Radar altimeters went a step further in allowing the commercial airliners to operate in lower weather minima safely. In the past, minimum ceilings of 200 feet were proscribed to allow for possible errors in barometric type altimeters close to the ground. The new devices provided an accuracy of plus or minus 1 percent, which permitted landings under still lower ceilings.

Today we have something still newer, to regulate airliner traffic in a way to eliminate holding patterns (and thereby save fuel) and permit ETA's within a matter of seconds: the Flight Management System. It couples completely automatic performance and navigation system to the airliner's autopilot and autothrottles.

Lockheed's Richard L. Heimbold, group engineer for advanced control systems, commenting on the first such FMS installed in an L-1011-200, explained: "What we are doing is using basically the same hardware, but introducing a sophisticated software program which makes the system four-dimensional—the fourth dimension being time. We call it the 4-FMS." In operation, all pertinent information, including weather conditions and wind factors, are plugged into an on-board computer. During the flight, the system continually monitors and updates all data and makes appropriate adjustments not only to insure precise arrival time, but also to fly the entire profile with minimum fuel consumption.

CRT Displays

Another system developed by Lockheed, the British Aerospace AFD Phase II System, utilizes a full panel of cathode ray tube (CRT) displays to replace the outmoded electro-mechanical dials and gauges used in the past.

All these space-age gadgets are fine, but the human element is still in the cockpit—the pilot, copilot, navigator, and observer. Midair collisions still occur when pilots fail to "eyeball" the sky completely, as on a busy ILS approach. To alleviate this hazard, the Federal Aviation Administration recently promulgated a new regulation that bars airline crews from engaging in non-essential duties during critical phases of flight.

What lies ahead in the airline industry?

Advanced technology airliners already are flying—the McDonnell Douglas DC-9 Super 80 twinjet transport was type-certificated in August 1980; Lockheed came out with its L-1011-500 long-range TriStar, and Boeing rolled out its first 767 three-engined transport, with their still-newer 757 twinjet scheduled for delivery in 1983.

The FAA continues to upgrade its Third Generation Air Traffic Control System. In 1980 the first En Route Safe Altitude Warning System (E-MSAW) was commissioned at the Cleveland Air Route Traffic Control Center. E-MSAW monitors the flight path of aircraft whose cockpits are equipped with altitude-encoding transponders for adequate terrain clearance, by comparing the airliner's flight path with a computer-stored grid map of the terrain involved.

A similar system already operational at 62 terminal areas is the ARTS-III automated radar system. It's already being upgraded with installation of a Conflict-Alert System to warn ATC controllers whenever aircraft are on converging courses.

Still in the future are hypersonic airliners capable of flying at Mach 6 (six times the speed of sound) powered with SCRAMJETS (Supersonic Combustion Ramjets). They will be able to carry passengers from San Francisco to Paris in less than 1½ hours, in the event you're in that big a hurry! SciFi buffs also are talking about laser energy to replace hydrocarbon fuels for futuristic airliners flying at the fringe of space, drawing on laser-beam energy from orbiting satellites.

And tomorrow—the stars?

Boeing 247D Transport.

Boeing 247D

The first all-metal cantilever monoplane commercial air transport with a retractable landing gear to attain quantity production, the Model 247 first flew February 8, 1933. Seventy-five aircraft of this type were built. In standard configuration, the 247 carried ten passengers and a crew of three.

The Boeing 247D (C-73) was an improved version of the original 247. No Model B or C was built. The Model 247D featured full NACA cowlings, fabric-covered movable tail surfaces, controllable-pitch propellers, and windscreens that sloped upward and aft. These features, plus gearing of the 14-cylinder

Pratt & Whitney Twin Wasp Jr. engines of 625 hp, gave the 247D a top speed of 200 mph. A total of twelve 247Ds were built.

One 247D was built for Col. Roscoe Turner and Clyde Pangborn as an entry in the 1934 MacRobertson air race from London to Melbourne, Australia. It ran second and later flew under United Air Lines colors. In 1942, 27 247Ds were drafted into the U.S. Army Air Corps as C-73s.

A roomy two-man cockpit was instrumented for "blind" flight. Fuel switchover valves were installed on a flat panel above the power console.

Cockpit of Boeing 247D. (courtesy Boeing)

Boeing 307 Stratoliner of 1939.

Boeing 307 Stratoliner

In 1937 the Collier Trophy was awarded to the U.S. Air Corps for developing the Lockheed XC-35 substratosphere plane as "the first pressurized cabin airplane to be flown successfully anywhere in the world." Two years later the Boeing Company took up the challenge and delivered to Pan American its Model 307 Stratoliner, the "Flying Cloud," the world's first commercial pressurized airliner.

With a circular cross-section, its fuselage was said to resemble a "dirigible with wings." The Stratoliner carried 33 passengers, had a span of 107 feet, and could climb to 23,300 feet. Powered with four Wright GR-1820 engines of 900 hp each, it cruised at 246 mph and had a range of 2390 miles. Ten Stratoliners were built by Boeing.

Above the cockpit's windscreen were an array of switches to operate the autopilot, turn on landing lights, or call the stewardess for coffee. Two sets of flight instruments were mounted at left and right on the panel, with a gyro compass in the center above the power console, below which were mounted the plane's radio and trimming wheels.

Cockpit of Boeing 307 Stratoliner. (courtesy Boeing)

Boeing Model 377 Stratocruiser.

Boeing Model 377 Stratocruiser

Boeing's Model 377 Stratocruiser was an airliner version of the military C-97 Stratofreighter, the first commercial Boeing aircraft built since the 314 Clipper. A total of 56 were built from 1947-49, offering a competitive advantage of long range (4600 miles) and unparalleled passenger comfort. A lower deck lounge could be reached via a spiral staircase from the passenger cabin, and up to 100 passengers could be carried, depending on the route's length.

With a span of 141 feet 3 inches, the Stratocruiser had a gross weight of 145,000 pounds, cruised at 300 mph, and had a top speed of 375 mph. It was powered with four Pratt & Whitney 3500-hp Wasp Majors.

In the accompanying photograph of the Stratocruiser's cockpit, the flight engineer (foreground) checks an array of engine instruments and switches that would baffle many general aviation pilots! Over the cockpit ceiling are circuit breakers and NAV/COMM switches, with standard flight instruments on the instrument panel before pilot and copilot.

Cockpit of Boeing Model 377 Stratocruiser. (courtesy Boeing)

Boeing 707. (courtesy Boeing)

Boeing 707

The American jet air transport era opened on July 15, 1954, with the maiden flight of a top-secret Boeing transport designated 367-80—known to its designers as the Dash Eighty, and to the public eventually as the Model 707. It was born of Boeing's realization that the Model 377 Stratocruiser was the "end of the line" for piston-engined planes—the future lay with jets.

The Boeing 707 became probably the world's most modified airplane as changes included new wing planforms and airfoils, powerplant modifications, new leading edge and trailing edge flaps, and an aft-mounted engine pod. One of the Dash Eighty's last major test programs included installation of direct lift control and blown flaps that enabled it to land at only 75 mph. The 367-80 Prototype now displayed at the National Air and Space Museum has been called "one of the most significant aircraft of all time."

The original production model, the 707-120, was built in both long-body and short-body versions. Largest of the 707 family are the Intercontinentals—the 707-320s and 707-420s, able to carry 189 passengers. The Improved 707-420B model was ordered by PanAm to become by far the longest-range jets in commercial service—six thousand miles.

Boeing 707 cockpit. (courtesy Boeing)

Boeing 727. (courtesy Boeing)

Boeing 727

The three-engined Boeing 727 grew out of market studies for a modern, short-to-medium range jet to replace many piston and turboprop engines planes in service. Three engines were chosen for economy and desired performance and the rear mounting was a logical choice for such a design.

The first 727 rolled out of the Boeing factory on November 27, 1962, and was flown for the first time the following February. Design range was from 150 to more than 1700 miles and early tests showed it could operate safely from mile-long runways. Production models would soon be flying 2500-mile routes.

The 727 was hailed as the first "Quick Change" airplane—flown during the day as a passenger plane and converted to all-cargo at night. It became the first commercial aircraft to surpass the 1000-sales mark for civilian use. It also was first to use the now-popular triple-slotted flap system for improved takeoff and landing performance.

Among advanced systems in the 727 is a performance data computer to assist crews in determining the most fuel-efficient thrust settings for each phase of flight. A central digital air data computer is tied to the cockpit instrumentation.

Boeing 727 cockpit. (courtesy Boeing)

Boeing 737. (courtesy Boeing)

Boeing 737

The Boeing 737 was announced in February, 1965, as a logical, short-range airplane to complement the bigger 707 and 727 jetliners. With a shorter fuselage, the first 737-100 flew on April 9, 1967, and the first 737-200, 6 feet longer, flew in December of that year. The 737-100 entered service with Lufthansa early in 1968, followed by United's inaugural flight with -200s on April 28. The twinjet quickly proved economical and popular.

Both models use Pratt & Whitney JT8D-7 turbofans of 14,000 pounds thrust. Certification included approval for a two-man flight crew and automatic approaches with a 100-foot ceiling and 1200 feet RVR (Runway Visual Range). By 1980 more than 760 737s had been ordered by 90 airlines and the USAF and some 600,000,000 passengers had been carried commercially.

Advanced versions of the 737 twinjet incorporate aerodynamic refinements, a stopping package with improved anti-skid and automatic brakes, and more powerful engines.

Newer 737s are fitted with a Performance Data Computer System (PDCS) as basic equipment. The Lear Siegler system gives crews advisory information on engine pressure ratios, temperatures, and airspeed, for maximum fuel efficiency.

Boeing 737 cockpit. (courtesy Boeing)

Boeing 747. (courtesy Boeing)

Boeing 747

First of the giant jumbo jet airliners, the Boeing 747 is the largest airplane ever built for commercial service. Its inception goes back to 1960s when Boeing saw a coming need for a jumbo jet to handle future expected airline passenger traffic and cargo loads for the 1970s and 1980s. Within a year of conception, Boeing had received $1.8 billion in orders for the superjets, one of the largest backlog orders in history.

Today more than 420 of the 747s have been rolled out, and since inauguration of service in January 1970, Boeing 747s have carried more than 280 million passengers and logged more than eight million hours of flight time. Able to carry 500 passengers, the interior volume of the 747 also revolutionized air transportation of outsize cargo.

A unique feature is the upper deck, immediately behind the cockpit, used to accommodate 32 passengers or as a luxury lounge.

A smaller version, the 747SP (Special Performance) is 47 feet shorter, designed to fly higher, faster and farther than any other wide-body airliner—it can carry 331 passengers more than 6000 miles nonstop on such runs as New York-to-Tokyo.

One 747-100 was modified by Boeing to ferry the NASA Space Shuttle Orbiter from landing sites back to its launch area at Cape Canaveral.

Boeing 747 cockpit. (courtesy Boeing)

Boeing 757. (courtesy Boeing)

Boeing 757

The Boeing 757 is a new twin-engine, short-to-medium range jetliner combining efficiency of the six-abreast fuselage arrangement with a new technology wing and engines to provide optimum fuel mileage. It can carry up to 233 passengers.

Fuselage length is 155 feet 3 inches, and its wing makes use of the same advanced technology used in the 767, with a span of 124½ feet. Its advanced flight deck employs the same technology concepts planned for the new 767 Boeing jetliners.

In a time of high fuel prices, the 757's fuel efficiency was an important design goal. On a 500-mile flight it burns some 40 percent less fuel per seat than other airliners it was designed to displace; thus in 1985 a fleet of ten 757s replacing 727-100s could save $15 million (in 1980 dollars) in fuel costs. The 757 is powered with two wing-mounted Rolls-Royce RB211-535C engines of 37,400 pounds thrust.

The new, efficient wing, fitted with double-slotted trailing edge flaps and full-span leading edge slats, permits short field takeoffs with 1250 feet less runway than the advanced 727. It also can cruise at altitudes 6000 feet higher than the 727-200. Initial flights were scheduled for early 1982.

Boeing 757 cockpit mock-up. (courtesy Boeing)

Boeing 767. (courtesy Boeing)

Boeing 767

In the Boeing 767 twinjet, an entirely new commercial passenger airplane design uses advanced technology to provide maximum efficiency in operating costs, while extending twin-aisle passenger cabin convenience to routes never before serviced by wide-body airliners. Production began with an order for 30 medium-range 767s from United Airlines in July of 1978. The 767 is the first Boeing airliner to go in to production since the 747 in 1966. Deliveries were scheduled to begin in August 1982.

The 767 is powered with two high-bypass-ratio turbofan engines manufactured either by General Electric or Pratt & Whitney, at the airlines' option.

With advanced design, high-lift wing flaps, the 767 requires a takeoff field length of about 5900 feet at maximum gross weight (282,000 pounds), or 6700 feet at 300,000 pounds gross. The advanced, Boeing-designed airfoil is thicker, longer, and has less sweepback than earlier Boeing jetliners.

In the medium-range version, the 767 can fly nonstop on such routes as Los Angeles-to-Miami or London-to-Cairo. Among the new cockpit goodies is a Honeywell ring-laser-gyro inertial reference system (IRS), replacing earlier mechanical displays.

Boeing 767 cockpit. (courtesy Boeing)

Prototype Concorde SST in flight. (courtesy British Aircraft Corporation)

Concorde SST

Under development since 1962, the British/French Concorde Supersonic Transport was certified for passenger-carrying in 1975 after two prototype flight, two pre-production, and four production Concordes had been built and the latter had flown more than 5000 hours. By January 1977, 14 Concordes had flown including 10 production models. First to fly was Concorde 001 on March 2, 1969; the second Concorde, 002, first flew on April 9, 1969.

In their first year of service, British Airways and Air France Concordes flew more than 45,000 passengers, mainly on the North Atlantic blue-ribbon routes. The production Concordes are powered with four Rolls-Royce/SNECMA Olympus 593 Mk 610 turbojets of 38,050 pounds thrust each, and up to 144 passengers can be carried.

Pilot and copilot sit side by side on the flight deck with the third crew member behind on starboard side. Max cruising speed is 1354 mph, range 4050 miles.

Cockpit of prototype Concorde SST. (courtesy British Aircraft Corporation)

Douglas DC-3 transport. (courtesy McDonnell Douglas)

Douglas DC-3

Douglas Aircraft Company launched its DC-3 program in 1935 following a telephone call from American Airlines President C.R. Smith ordering a fleet of 20 with options for 20 more, at $110,000 each. First flight of a DC-3 took place on December 17, 1935, the anniversary of the first Wright Brothers flight at Kitty Hawk. Part of American's order included DC-3s fitted with sleeping berths for 16 passengers.

By the end of the decade, the DC-3 was carrying 95 percent of all air passenger traffic in the United States. It became the USAF's beloved C-47 "Gooney Bird," the Navy and Marines' R4D, the British Dakota, and a total of 10,691 were built. Douglas won the 1935 Collier Trophy "for the development of outstanding twin-engine transports".

The standard DC-3 carried two 1200-horsepower Pratt & Whitney R-1830 radial engines; the Super DC-3 had two Wright 1820s of 1475 hp each. Up to 28 passengers could be carried at 167 knots cruise speed for a range of 1300 nautical miles in the standard model. Flight instruments were at the left in the DC-3 panel, engine instruments at right, power console at center.

Cockpit of Douglas DC-3.

Douglas DC-4 transport.

Douglas DC-4

In 1936, five major airlines joined to have Douglas design a new four-engined transport, the first such instance of a cooperative reequipment effort in the airline industry—American, Eastern, Pan American, TWA, and United. They asked for a capacity of 40 passengers, 230 mph top speed, 140-foot span and a two-engine altitude of 9000 feet.

War in Europe broke out before full production started on a commercial DC-4; hence it first served in the military as the Air Force C-54 troop carrier, the Skymaster. The original concept was felt to be too big for economic operation, hence the DC-4A evolved with a span of 117½ feet, though it carried 42 people. Many military C-54s were converted to commercial use after the war, and another 79 were built to carry 44 passengers before production halted in 1947. More than 260 remain in service worldwide.

Radios on power console, Air France DC-4.

The cockpits of Air France DC-4s mounted radio controls on the control pedestal, behind the throttles and above the ganged mixture controls, supercharger levers, and flap and cowl controls. Both pilot and copilot had primary IFR instruments, with the engine gauges at center.

Copilot's and center panel of Air France DC-4.

Douglas DC-6 transport. (courtesy McDonnell Douglas)

Douglas DC-6

World War II was drawing to a close when Douglas Aircraft Company developed their DC-6 as a more powerful, stretched and pressurized version of the popular DC-4/C-54 Skymaster. The DC-6 first flew on February 15, 1946, as a military transport for the USAAF, designated the XC-112A, and deliveries to the airlines began early the following year. Externally it closely resembled the DC-4, but the fuselage was 7 feet longer, and the former porthole-shaped windows were replaced with rectangular openings.

Carrying capacity was upped to 68 passengers, while some DC-6s were later modified for air coach operations with a capacity of 85 passengers. In all, 175 DC-6s were built, and some even went to the Luftwaffe. Two versions besides the standard DC-6 were the DC-6A and DC-6B. All were powered with four engines—the standard DC-6 used the Pratt & Whitney R-2800CB16 of 2400 horsepower, and the DC-6A & 6B the Pratt & Whitney R-2800CB17 of 2500 horsepower each. Gross weights were from 95,200 to 107,000 pounds, depending on the model. Maximum cruise at 20,400 feet was 315 mph, max range 4480 miles. The cockpit arrangement was similar to that of the DC-4s.

Cockpit of Douglas DC-6. (courtesy McDonnell Douglas)

Douglas DC-7B transport. (courtesy McDonnell Douglas)

Douglas DC-7B

Douglas Aircraft Company's ultimate piston-engined airliner developed from the prewar DC-4 was their DC-7. Three models were built—the standard, which first flew May 18, 1953, the DC-7B, which first flew April 21, 1955, and the DC-7C, that got off the ground December 20, 1955. The latter version featured a wider span than its predecessors (extended at the roots), a 3-foot longer fuselage, taller tail, increased fuel tankage, and accommodations for 58 first class or 99 coach class seats. The "C" model was designated to fly the North Atlantic routes nonstop.

The DC-7B passenger version cruised at 290 knots, and the cargo version ten knots slower, while the uprated DC-7C cruised at 315 knots (362 mph). The "B" model used four 3250-hp Wright R-3350 engines, the "C" model four 3350s uprated to 3400 hp.

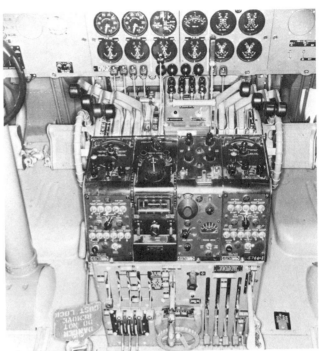

DC-7B radio controls on control pedestal. (courtesy McDonnell Douglas)

The cockpit instrument panel of the DC-7 was advanced for the 1950s, with autopilot and NAV/COMMs installed in the power console. Both pilot and copilot had four throttle levers to fight over.

Full panel and control pedestal of DC-7B. (courtesy McDonnell Douglas)

Douglas DC-8. (courtesy McDonnell Douglas)

Douglas DC-8

Douglas Aircraft Company entered the commercial jet field on Memorial Day, 1958, with the maiden flight of its first DC-8 from Long Beach Municipal Airport. The prototype was actually a DC-8-10, powered with four Pratt & Whitney turbofans of 13,500 pounds thrust each, which provided a cruise speed at 35,000 feet of 570 mph.

In 1961, a production DC-8 actually flew faster than sound in a test hop at Edwards AFB, reaching a speed of Mach 1.012 at 41,088 feet, to demonstrate structural integrity of the jetliner. Within a decade the DC-8 had grown 37 feet in length with the DC-8 Super 63F, with a gross takeoff weight of 355,000 pounds—177.5 tons. The Super 63F could carry 259 economy-class passengers and had a range of 6000 miles.

A redesign of the DC-8 cockpit featured two attitude indicators, one at the center of each flight panel, engine gauges at center panel, and a more streamlined power console. Ram air and static air temperature indicators were added, along with other instrumentation required to monitor the four Pratt & Whitney JT3D-7 engines of 19,000 pounds thrust each.

Cockpit of Douglas DC-8. (courtesy McDonnell Douglas)

Douglas DC-9 Super 80. (courtesy McDonnell Douglas)

Douglas DC-9

The McDonnel DC-9 was designed for short-field operation on short-to-medium routes, carried a high T-tail and had two fanjet engines mounted on the aft fuselage. Six DC-9 versions were built—Series 10, 20, 30, 40, 50, and Super 80. The first prototype flew February 25, 1965, and several models in each series offered a wide range of designs tailored for maximum efficiency under diverse combinations of traffic density, cargo volume, and route distances from 100 miles to more than 2000 miles.

The DC-9 Super 80, powered with two Pratt & Whitney JT8D-217 engines of 20,000 pounds thrust each, can carry 137 passengers 2100 miles at 557 mph

and operate from the same runways as the lower-powered models.

Advanced technology designed into the Super 80 included for the first time in a DC-9 such features as a new digital electronics integrated flight guidance and control system for extended minimum weather operations; a "dial-a-flap" system for most efficient takeoff and landing performance; and flow-through cooling of the aircraft's avionics equipment. It also has a Mark IIIA antiskid system, electronic engine synchronization system, dual automatic electronic pressurization system, and weather radar with digitalized display. Maiden flight of the Super 80 was in October, 1979.

Cockpit of Douglas DC-9. (courtesy McDonnell Douglas)

Douglas DC-10-30. (courtesy McDonnell Douglas)

Douglas DC-10

When the first Douglas DC-10 made its maiden flight on August 29, 1970, a new category of airplane was added to the world's air transportation system. The three-engine jet transport incorporated advances in propulsion, aerodynamics, structure, avionics, flight control systems and environmental compatibility. All models of the new trijet carry from 250 mixed passengers to 380 in the all-economy configuration. First commercial flight took place August 5, 1971, on American Airlines' Los Angeles-to-Chicago run.

Five models of the DC-10 can handle routes from 300 to 4000 statute miles, the Dash 10 version powered by General Electric CF6-6 jet engines of 40,000 pounds takeoff thrust each. The Series 30 intercontinental version uses advanced G.E. CF6-50 fanjets of 51,000 pounds thrust, and weighs 555,000 pounds gross. Wingspan is 165 feet 4 inches, and wings are swept 35 degrees.

The DC-10's roomy flight deck accommodates a three-man crew and two observers. Large windscreens offer good visibility. Crew seats feature electric-powered adjustment for comfort. The DC-10 has been certified for automatic landings under Category IIIA minimum weather conditions.

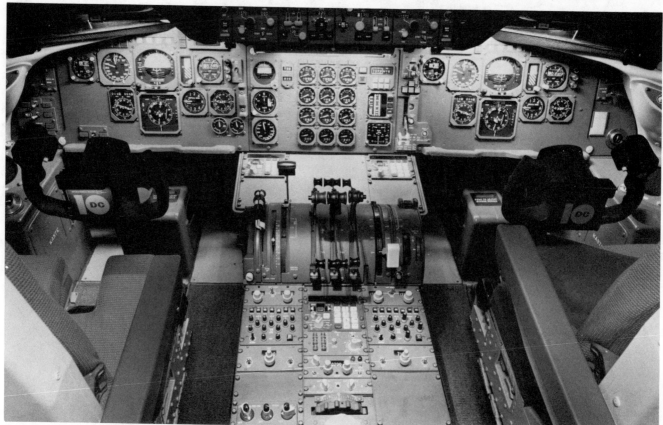

Douglas DC-10-30 cockpit. (courtesy McDonnell Douglas)

Lockheed Vega Winnie Mae. (courtesy Lockheed)

Lockheed Vega

The Model 1 Vega light commercial transport was the first plane produced by the newly formed Lockheed Aircraft Company. It first flew on the Fourth of July, 1927. Refined versions continued in production until 1934 when the 131st and last Vega was delivered to W. P. Fuller (it crashed in El Paso in 1945, killing the pilot, Raymond Darwin).

Most famous of the Vegas was *Winnie Mae*, named for the daughter of an Oklahoma oilman, F.C. Hall, whose personal pilot was a former oilfield roughneck—Wiley Post. Post twice circled the globe in *Winnie Mae*, first in 1931 with navigator Harold Gatty in 8 days, 15 hours, 51 minutes, to beat the 1929 record of the *Graf Zeppelin* of 21 days, 7 hours, 34 minutes.

In 1933, Post decided to repeat the world flight alone, replacing Gatty with black boxes including a Sperry Automatic Pilot and a borrowed U.S. Army directional radio (the autopilot failed over Russia and a local mechanic at Irkutsk fixed it). He finished the solo world flight in 7 days 18 hours 49 minutes to break his earlier record.

In 1934-35, Post used *Winnie Mae* to pioneer high-altitude flights, increasing his supercharged aircraft's performance from 192 mph to 340 mph in the thin air of the substratosphere. Wearing his famous "Man from Mars" pressurized suit, Post once reached an altitude of 55,000 feet. Today the *Winnie Mae* is displayed at the National Air and Space Museum.

Winnie Mae cockpit. (courtesy Lockheed)

Lockheed 9-C Orion. (courtesy Lockheed)

Lockheed 9-C Orion

Lockheed introduced the six-passenger Orion commercial transport in 1930. True to Lockheed's tradition of naming their planes after heavenly stars and constellations, the Orion was preceded by the "Sirius" and the "Altair." Before the CAA banned single-engine passenger transports on major airlines, Orions flew with American Airlines, Northwest Airways and other carriers.

Powered with 550-hp Pratt & Whitney Wasps,

they could climb at 1450 fpm; utilizing the first wing flaps ever installed on a Lockheed plane, the Orion could land at 55 mph and carry more payload.

The Orion pilot sat in an open cockpit with sliding canopy for cold weather operation. When Wiley Post retired his faithful *Winnie Mae*, he picked up TWA's third Orion and used it to fly to Alaska with Will Rogers on their ill-fated trip that ended in tragedy in 1935.

Lockheed Orion cockpit. (courtesy Lockheed)

Lockheed Model 14. (courtesy Lockheed)

Lockheed Model 14

A fascinating story lies behind Lockheed's Model 14 Super Electra twin-engined transport that first flew July 29, 1937, with space for three crew members and 11 passengers. One was purchased by Howard Hughes, who installed the most advanced instruments then available—an improved Sperry gyro-pilot with remote control; Sperry directional gyros and artificial horizons; two radio compasses, one for homing, one for triangulation; timing and navigational devices built to order by Longines; a line-of-position computer for navigational bearings; and three separate radios. The cost was $300,000, which HH paid out-of-pocket.

Lockheed Model 14 cockpit. (courtesy Lockheed)

A worldwide weather reporting network furnished daily broadcasts every half-hour, based on 900 observations, via a chain of local stations around the globe. With a crew of three, Hughes circled the world in 3 days 19 hours 17 minutes, covering 14,824 miles. He won the coveted Collier Trophy that said: "To Howard Hughes and his associates for their epoch-making round-the-world flight . . . involving notable advances in aerial navigation, communications and engineering; demonstrated the value of organization and planning in long-range aircraft operation; and afforded a world-wide demonstration of the superiority of American aviation products and techniques."

Shortly before World War II, a military version, the Model 414, was hastily assembled to show to the British Purchasing Commission looking for warplanes. The British ordered 250, and the first Hudson I flew on December 10, 1938. Additional Hudsons were ordered under the Lend-Lease Act in April 1941, and by May 1943, some 2522 had been delivered.

Many of these went across the North Atlantic to England, while a special ferry route was set up from Burbank to Great Falls, Montana, where Russian pilots picked them up to ferry to the Eastern Front. Almost forgotten is the fact that the United States, under Lend-Lease, supplied Russia with $10,982,089,000 in military equipment, including 14,695 aircraft.

Lockheed L.749 prototype. (courtesy Lockheed)

Lockheed L.749 Constellation

Lockheed's famous old triple-tail L. 749 Constellation transport originated at the Burbank plane factory as the XB-30, a design competition for a long-range bomber able to strike at Fortress Europe during World War II in the event England fell. General H. H. (Hap) Arnold called for proposals for a plane with a range of 5333 miles carrying a ton of bombs.

Though the competition was won by Boeing's XB-29, the Lockheed XB-30 finally appeared in transport form as the L.049 initially and first flew on January 9, 1943. Designed as a commercial transport, it nevertheless went into production as the C-69 and the

first 20 went to the USAAF.

After that came the L.149 version, 68 of which were assembled at the factory from C-69 components. The first true commercial version of the Connie was the L.649, with Wright R-3350-C18-BD1 engines. The L.749 was a long-range version with extra fuel in the outer wing panels. The L.749A's weight was upped from 105,000 to 107,000 pounds. A total of 133 L.749s and L.749As was built. Cockpits were fitted with standard gyro instrument panels. The Connie cruised at 298 mph at 60 percent power and had a V_{max} of 347 mph. Normal range was 3000 miles or 5500 miles maximum.

Cockpit of Lockheed L.749 Constellation. (courtesy Lockheed)

Lockheed L-1011-500 TriStar. (courtesy Lockheed)

Lockheed L-1011-500 TriStar

Lockheed's wide-bodied L-1011 TriStar first flew in November 1970, and in May 1972 an L-1011 flown by a Lockheed crew made the first fully automatic flight coast-to-coast, without human hands on the controls, takeoff to touchdown.

Newest and longest-range member of the L-1011 family is the Dash-500 model, designed to replace aging 707 and DC-8 competitive aircraft in low traffic density, long-haul markets. The L-1011-500 can fly 6100 miles nonstop. Early in 1981, Air Canada put its first L-1011-500 into service between Vancouver and London, one of a fleet of six 246-seat jetliners.

The L-1011-500's roomy flight compartment pro-vides stations for three crew members and two ob-servers; the ceiling is more than 6 feet high. The compartment has storage space for four large suit-cases, with space by each seat for flight kits. Four independent hydromechanical flight control systems provide easy handling of the huge aircraft, and Direct Lift Control (DLC) may be used for manual or automatic landings, using the Flight Control Electronics System (FCES).

The L-1011 Automated Navigation System pro-vides automatic guidance and control from airport ramp to airport ramp. The area navigation system (RNAV) consists of dual ARINC 582 MARK II RNAVs and dual ARINC 571 inertial sensor systems.

Cockpit of Lockheed L-1011-500 TriStar.

Space Shuttle Columbia on final approach.

Space Shuttle Columbia

Sometimes referred to as the "ultimate aerospaceliner." NASA'S Space Shuttle Columbia was built by Rockwell International Space Systems Group. It is the prime element of the U.S. Space Transportation System (STS), for space research and future applications including logistical transport support of future space stations. The Shuttle Orbiter is a manned spacecraft that can touch down on a landing strip like a giant airliner and therefore is reusable. Its primary function is to deliver payloads to Earth orbit. On a standard mission, the Orbiter will remain in orbit for 7 days, return to Earth with the flight crew and payloads, land like an airplane, and be ready for a next flight within 14 days.

The Orbiter's flight deck contains the displays and controls used to pilot, monitor, and control the Orbiter, the Integrated Shuttle Vehicles, and mission payloads, with seating for up to four crew members. The mid-deck contains passenger seating, living area, airlock, galley, sleeping compartments, toilet, and avionics equipment compartments. A lower deck contains the environmental control equipment, accessible through a removable floor panel.

Cockpit of Space Shuttle Columbia.

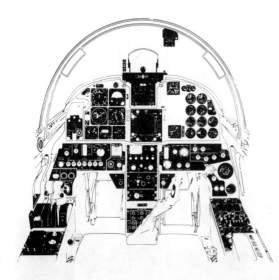

Chapter 11
Glass Cockpits

Today's airliner flight decks, marvels that they are, are rapidly being modified to take advantage of integrated circuits and microprocessors as cheap, reliable, and basic elements of electronic architecture, say J. W. Wilson and R. E. Hillman of British Aerospace. Based on lengthy studies of pilot performance in a BAC 111 simulator (Fig. 11-1), they report "striking improvements in the quality and ease of communication and navigation, which in turn have brought about the demise of the dedicated radio operator and navigator. The trend will continue with more automation of flight control and system management leading to two-crew operation of the majority of short- and medium-range aircraft, providing that flight safety standards continue to improve."

The most significant factor to influence the transport aircraft flight deck, they feel, has been, and will continue to be the development and application of avionic equipment. Digital machines now being introduced will provide civil aircraft with a computing power that will not be fully exploited for many years, they believe. "This capability most profitably will be used to improve the economy of air transportation and to achieve an ever higher level of safety."

Minimum Crew

The advanced flight deck, they point out, must ensure that the minimum crew can make a maximum use of the new equipment, both in the normal automatic mode of operation and when partial failures occur, or planned profiles have to be rapidly modified. For manual proficiency reasons, they state, "it seems very desirable that the crew should be able to achieve comparable flight profile and thrust management performance without the use of autopilot or autothrottle, with an acceptable, if higher, workload. Novel three-dimensional and thrust directors will be required for these purposes."

A key to improvement in layout and content of the main instrument panel, they say, is the use of cathode ray tube (CRT) displays (Fig. 11-2). These in turn, improve the layout of glareshield, pedestal, and overhead panel. Many of today's established flight deck requirements will continue to be valid over the next two decades:

☐ From 40 to 42 inches between pilot and first officer center lines and a 3-ARINC-width center pedestal.
☐ Basic-T flight data displays located on each pilot's center line.
☐ Flight and navigation displays unobstructed visually by cutoff from the control column and handwheel.
☐ Upper line of the glareshield giving a horizontal reference and 17 degrees downward vision; the lower line compatible with the required center panel display area.
☐ Much-used center pedestal controls located forward of the pilot's shoulder line.
☐ Overhead panel width and position compatible with the need for both pilots to reach all systems controls.

In the BAC 111 simulator a total of seven CRT displays are used. Three are grouped at center, and two each are grouped at pilot and copilot position, for good reason. "To cover loss of more than two CRTs," they say, "conventional standby displays of attitude, altitude, airspeed, heading and VOR/ADF, and engine EPR and TGT are required in the central panel area."

The glareshield width has been increased substantially, compared to today's aircraft, "to provide the largest possible control area containing all the switches and selectors associated with managing the electronic flight instrument displays and a four-dimensional flight guidance system."

Fig. 11-1. BAC 111 advanced cockpit layout.

The large, easy-to-reach glareshield makes possible the removal of all important controls from the main instrument panel and elimination of the undesirable forward stretch of arms and body.

Pedestal Layout

The pedestal of the BAC 111 simulator is divided into a forward area containing control and display units (CDU) for dual-route management systems

Fig. 11-2. Seven CRTs in BAC 111 simulator panel.

(RMS) and an aft area for aircraft system display control and radio frequency management. RMS CDUs are closely integrated with the flight and navigation CRT displays and therefore are located in the best position for keyboard operation by either pilot.

Routine management of aircraft systems is carried out in the overhead panel. The relevant data are presented on either of the center CRTs automatically on fault detection or manually from either system display controller.

Two additional RMS CDUs are located in the outer pedestal, from which either pilot may elect to control and display documentation, other navigational aids, or data links. Documentation in the form of checklists, abnormal drills, and emergency drills is displayed on either of the navigation or system CRTs in association with an item identifier controlled from the stick hub. Of prime importance is the ability to display all flight and system data compactly within the head-down scan of a two-man crew, while use of keyboards to insert data into digital computers is considered inevitable.

Color CRTs are used to avoid the visual flatness of monochrome and to provide emphasis and discrimination. Three-gun colors with 50 percent mixes and white and black give a close approximation to the color range conventionally used for flight deck display.

Navigation data are presented on a "conventional" compass rose or on a symbolic map with or without weather radar. With either format, digital radio and navigation data are shown periphally.

Glareshield Layout

The glareshield provides the best available position in terms of reach and sightline for those selectors relating to flight guidance and flight/navigation display control. Furthermore, to reduce hand movement, some flight guidance controls conventionally found in the glareshield panel have been located on the pilot's control wheel, for use in the more dynamic flight conditions.

The pilot may select any system format for presentation on the two center CRT displays, via either of the aft pedestal system display select controllers. When automatic operation is selected, any failure that activates the master warning system causes automatic presentation of the relevant format and, in the lower part of the same display, the associated emergency drill or abnormal drill.

The master warning system includes a voice alert message subsystem—a bell for fire, wailer for autopilot or autothrottle disconnect, horn of two seconds duration for speed or altitude deviation, a whoop for ground proximity, three attention tones every five seconds for emergency items, two tones every 15 seconds until cancelled for Level 2 (immediate recognition) items, and one tone for Level 1 (awareness) item.

The simulator's overhead panel contains conventional system controls in the form of push-on/push-off buttons with integral annunciation of current mode and system failure. All data indications are remotely displayed in either of the system CRTs, for which the format is a close mimic of the panel layout.

To cater for safe operation after loss of all CRT displays, sufficient intelligence is provided in the warning indications to ensure that pushing a lit button will control the associated fault without reference to its system display.

Improvements have been made in reducing the amount of paperwork and transcription involved in today's flight deck operation. CRT displays are the key element in presentation of checks relating to phase of flight from preflight to shutdown.

Other improvements include presentation of meteorological and ATIS information and ATC clearances using ADSEL/DABS data link, to significantly reduce the workload currently associated with obtaining critical MET data in poor weather conditions, and will minimize ATC communications throughout the flight. Another system allows teletyping of data link information to allow unhurried verification by the crew using hard copy and reduction of the paperwork obtained at preflight briefing.

Safety First

"The prime objective in flight deck design," they say, "is to ensure that the crew can control and monitor the aircraft and its systems to achieve a precise and economical flight path with safety at an optimum level of workload, in both normal and abnormal conditions."

Looking ahead to implementation of the simulator design in active aircraft, new digital equipment for automatic flight management, thrust control, frequency selection, and electronic color displays has now been ordered and is being built. The required technology is available to implement data link, collision avoidance, MLS, NAVSTAR, and SATCOM systems.

In summation, the study concludes that "it is unlikely that today's widebody jets and new aircraft entering service in the next five years will be replaced by a new generation before the end of the century, but the pressure for improvement in economy and safety that the new equipment can provide will result in progressive introduction of the features described. If the benefits are to be realized in the next few years, the active support of airlines, vendors, and certification authorities will be required."

Index